THE LEGACY OF ANNE FRANK

Anne Frank is known to the world for the famous diary in which she recorded the events of her tragic life. Actually, that diary is only a part of the literary legacy she created. She also wrote reminiscences and stories about her friends, her school, her teachers; even about the handsome young man who shared her hideout during the war. She wrote fables about bears and elves and lonely girls. Like her diary, these other works are filled with the same sense of youth and tenderness and unquenchable faith which has inspired millions.

ANNE FRANK'S UNFINISHED NOVEL
CADY'S LIFE
IS INCLUDED IN
TALES FROM THE HOUSE BEHIND

BANTAM PATHFINDER EDITIONS

Bantam Pathfinder Editions provide the best in
fiction and nonfiction in a wide variety of
subject areas. They include novels by classic
and contemporary writers; vivid, accurate
histories and biographies; authoritative works
in the sciences; collections of short
stories, plays and poetry.

Bantam Pathfinder Editions are carefully
selected and approved. They are durably bound,
printed on specially selected high-quality paper,
and presented in a new and handsome format.

TALES FROM
THE HOUSE BEHIND

BY ANNE FRANK

Introduction by
Ann Birstein and Alfred Kazin
Drawings by Peter Spier

BANTAM  BOOKS, INC.

BANTAM PATHFINDER EDITIONS
NEW YORK / TORONTO / LONDON

RLI: VLM 6.0
IL 7.12

TALES FROM THE HOUSE BEHIND

*A Bantam Book / published by arrangement with
Doubleday & Company, Inc.*

PRINTING HISTORY

*First published in the United Kingdom
by the World's Work (1913) Ltd.
Pan Books edition published 1965
Bantam Pathfinder edition published September 1966
2nd printing*

*Bantam Books are published by Bantam Books, Inc., a subsidiary
of Grosset & Dunlap, Inc. Its trade-mark, consisting of the words
"Bantam Books" and the portrayal of a bantam, is registered in the
United States Patent Office and in other countries. Marca Registrada.
Bantam Books, Inc., 271 Madison Avenue, New York, N. Y. 10016.*

Contents

PUBLISHER'S NOTE

The dates on the stories and essays are those that Anne herself gave them when she wrote them in her notebook. In the case of *Rita* and *Why?* and *Cady's Life* there are no dates, because they were not included in the notebook but were discovered on separate sheets of paper.

Cady's Life was translated by H. H. B. Mosberg and all the other material by Michel Mok.

On pages 53, 100, and 117 are reproductions from Anne Frank's actual manuscripts.

Introduction

BY ANN BIRSTEIN AND ALFRED KAZIN

In March 1945, a young girl died in Bergen-Belsen, unaware that she was leaving behind her a work that shed the first tiny human light on an episode in history that was unspeakably inhuman. She was a lovely girl, not quite sixteen when she died, with enormous dark gray eyes, a pretty little mouth, and a very brave heart. But like any awkward and self-conscious adolescent, she was weighed down by a sense of her shortcomings. She worried about her looks; she thought of herself as a coward, so often full of fear that she never realized how heroically she overcame it. Certainly, it would have been beyond her to imagine that the diary she kept for two years would have an impact on the entire world; how could it when the events of her lifetime were so enormous she could only seem puny by comparison? Her only real certainty was that she meant to be a writer anyway, and that her subject would have to be the world in which she found herself alive, no matter how terrible or even how unaccountably lovely her experiences in it might seem. For two years before her arrest she wrote all the time. She wrote while she was in hiding from the Nazis and could not take one step outdoors or in the day-time speak above a whisper. She wrote although the bombs came down so heavily at night that she fled for comfort into her father's bed. She wrote so steadily that by the time she was fifteen she had finished the equivalent of two books, one the *Diary*, the other a collection of short stories, essays, and reminiscences. As she said, with amazement at her own daring, she wrote because, "I want to go on living even after my death!" She has—reminding us that each of those millions who died in agony and despair, each of those victims whom the Nazis "exterminated" was, like Anne Frank, a separate and precious human spirit.

Of Anne Frank's actual life, as apart from her work, there is very little to tell; she did not live to see her sixteenth birthday. But because she had a great capacity for happiness, her life all in all was quite a happy one. She was born in Frankfurt, Germany on June 12, 1929, to fairly wealthy Jewish parents, and she was lucky in her family, for although no one in her lifetime considered her unusual or profound, she was always able to count on a great deal of love and mutual respect in her home. She had a grandmother whom she adored and whom she refers to both in her diary and her stories as a "guardian angel," and an older sister, Margot, who was by everyone's account both beautiful and kind. With her mother she got on less well, though her complaints are largely just the usual ones of any growing girl. Actually, her mother taught Anne a great deal, especially lessons in charity. "No one ever becomes poor from giving," Mrs. Frank used to say, and Anne herself repeats this in her little essay called "Give." But it was her father Anne loved best, and with reason. He was and is a cultured man of great personal nobility and quiet courage, exactly the kind of father an adolescent girl could always turn to. In 1933, when Hitler came to power, the Franks moved to Amsterdam, and though life soon closed in on them—the Franks, no longer wealthy, had to take in boarders; Holland was invaded and capitulated to Germany; the Nazis issued strict anti-Jewish decrees; Anne had to leave the Montessori School, which she had loved, and go to the Jewish Lyceum—Anne remained the same humorous child she had always been. Lies Goosens, an old school friend in Amsterdam, who later saw Anne in Belsen, remembers her being considered a "problem child, very talkative"; by Mr. Frank's own tender confession, she never in life seemed so "deep" as she appeared in her diary. She was a vivid girl, but definitely not a prodigy. Ironically enough, the very vividness and intensity of the adolescent self-confrontation that was to make the *Diary* famous perhaps made Anne seem more conventional than she really was. The headmistress of the Montessori School in Amsterdam (now the Anne Frank School) remembers that Anne did not show any early promise, and that many of her pupils wrote with more imagination and feeling than did Anne. When we read the accounts of those who had known Anne, we can see that although she had always been very distinct to them and often arresting, she had been seen only as a very young girl, and externally very much a girl of her own age. She had a passion for movie stars, whose pictures she collected, and for royalty—one of her main preoccupations was the difficulty of finding suitable husbands for Princess Elizabeth and Princess Margaret of Great Britain. She was a great talker, often an incessant one, as her family and teachers knew only too well, and her fondness for make-believe was such that she would bring a suitcase along even when she was just visiting for an hour next door. Anne giggled with her girl friends, was saucy and flirtatious with boys, played a lot of ping-pong, and consumed great quantities of ice cream afterward. She had a lovely thirteenth birthday with a party, home movies, flowers, and many presents, among them a small clothbound diary which Anne decided at once was "possibly the nicest of all." Then, a month after this birthday, life closed in on the Franks for good. On a hot July morning in 1942 they went into hiding, walking across Amsterdam in the pouring rain to a small group of rooms behind Mr. Frank's former offices. Here they and four others were to stay cooped up for more than two years, until the Dutch Green Police routed them out on August 4, 1944; and here Anne's diary, that nice present, was to grow and grow until, like all truly remarkable books, it finally outgrew its own author.

In a certain sense, however, it isn't fair to call *The Diary of a Young Girl* a diary at all, since from the very first it was more to her than a purely personal record of triumphs and defeats. Always she had toward her own experience the marvelous ambivalence of the born novelist, and immediately after claiming that "neither I—nor for that matter anyone else—will be interested in the unbosomings of a thirteen-year-old schoolgirl," on the very same page of her journal she has already chosen a literary form—the entries will be in the shape of letters to an imaginary girl named Kitty—and embarked on a concise sketch, not only of her own life, but of general conditions in Holland. This same uncanny sense of an unseen audience, actually of posterity, prevails throughout her work. Scared out of her wits as she must have been when she went into hiding, one of the first things she writes about it is a detailed description of the hiding place and the bits and pieces of furnishings that went into it. When new people arrive, first the Van Daans and then Dussel, the dentist, she has them down on paper practically the minute they are through the door. With a writer's eye for how much is implied in the ordinary events of an ordinary day, she describes a typical morning, afternoon, and evening in the annex; how they went to the toilet; where they slept; what they talked about while they peeled potatoes and shelled peas and stuffed sausages. She fell in love with the boy upstairs, yearned desperately for her first kiss, and in the breathless moment before it finally came broke into tears—which she described meticulously: "I sat pressed closely against him and felt a wave of emotion come over me, tears sprang into my eyes, the left one trickled onto his dungarees, the right one ran down my nose and also fell onto his dungarees. Did he notice? He made no move or sign to show that he did. . . . At half past eight I stood up and went to the window, where we always say goodby. . . . He came toward me, I flung my arms around his neck and gave him a kiss on his left cheek, and was about to kiss the other cheek, when my lips met his and we pressed them together."

To everything that happened to her, to everything that she felt, Anne gave a kind of permanence by transcribing it, and day after day she went on adding still another segment to the world she was creating. In the stories, where she chose her subjects, this world is not so real. But in her diary, where her subject chose her, its vividness and poignance are overwhelming. We can see them all: Mrs. Frank, always a little in the shadows, defending the upbringing of her children, or discussing with Mrs. Van Daan the best way to address servants; Mrs. Van Daan taking time out for a little flirtation with Dussel, the pompous old dentist, or else picking a fight with Mr. Van Daan ("But Putti . . . Mr. Frank always answers his wife, doesn't he?"); young, shy Peter Van Daan lying listlessly in his cluttered boy's room upstairs; Margot, always composed and gentle; Mr. Frank putting aside his beloved Dickens to settle a quarrel and put things right again; their Dutch protectors coming upstairs with their thoughtful little presents and their tantalizing whiffs of the outside world; and Anne, working out her genealogical tables, pasting up her pictures of movie stars, talking so much that everyone has to tell her to shut up—and then transforming herself into the ninth member, the one who retired to the little table so hard won from Mr. Dussel to bring the others to life. What makes her achievement really amazing is how little, aside from her own natural gifts of observation and her sense of humor, she had to work with. Other people have countrysides and multitudes. For Anne, the one boy upstairs was love; a single chestnut tree seen from her window, nature; a patch of blue sky— heaven. No wonder that soon she began to think of her diary and some of her sketches as the basis for a book after the war. *Het Achterhuis* (The House Behind) she meant to call it— a perfect title for the first book of a young girl, suggesting mystery and suspense and excitement; she even had a list of pseudonyms for the people in it, pseudonyms which are used in this present edition.

But the duality of Anne's nature, that quality of mind that made her turn to her writing for solace and relief, that made of her diary her "only friend" and the first thing she packed when she went into hiding, was exactly what would not let her rest. Like all young growing things, Anne, forced into a premature ripeness by the terrible intensity of events, yearned and struggled for the light. It was not enough to take her own little part in the day's happenings, to chatter and laugh and cry with everyone else; the spectator in her kept pressing her to ask the meaning of it all, kept goading her into a search that could only take her deeper and deeper into the most pain-

[5]

ful realms of solitude. We tend to think of Anne now as pure innocence in captivity. But her mind and heart were never held captive by herself or anyone, and as for her innocence— it was the last thing she ever thought about. On the contrary, she wanted to take it all on her own shoulders, she considered herself responsible for everything, not only her own destiny— if she was permitted to live it out—but also the fate of every-one else who suffered. ". . . I believe," she said, "that God wants to try me . . ." And this theme of being tested through confinement is repeated in her stories of Blurry, the Explorer, the bear who goes out to see the world and is locked up in-stead, and of Dora and Peldron, the two elves who are im-prisoned by a wise dwarf and emerge improved by their experience. Somehow, Anne, too, would come out a better person, if only she were good and strong enough. Of course it was hard, agonizingly hard, to keep herself to such a strict moral accounting, especially when everything outside beck-oned so sweetly: "The sun is shining, the sky is a deep blue, there is a lovely breeze and I'm longing—so longing—for everything. To talk, for freedom, for friends, to be alone. And I do so long . . . to cry! I feel as if I'm going to burst, and I know that it would get better with crying; but I can't, I'm restless, I go from one room to the other, breathe through the crack of a closed window, feel my heart beating, as if it is saying, 'Can't you satisfy my longings at last?' . . . I believe that it's spring within me, I feel that spring is awakening. I feel it in my whole body and soul." But still she kept at it, crying herself out when she could, and then trying to unloose her own pity for herself into a great stream of compassion for all suffering humanity. How could she feel sorry for herself when just outside her door children were running about half naked, begging food from passers-by, and people did not dare leave their homes for fear that when they came back no one would be left in them? It was not enough to be glad of her own precarious safety; one had to ask why even this was de-nied others. She dreamed of her friend Lies Goosens, whom she imagined to have been sent to a concentration camp, and woke in tears: "Oh, God, that I should have all I could wish for and that she would be seized by such a terrible fate. I am not more virtuous than she; she, too, wanted what was right, why should I be chosen to live and she probably to die?" And what about all Jews? What purpose was there in their common agony? "Who has inflicted this upon us? What has made us different from other people? Who has allowed us to suffer so terribly until now?"

Child or not, anyone who asks such questions can never find an answer, only the strength of spirit to go on searching. Anne found her strength in her love of the very world which was denied her. Often in their "Secret Annex" they talked of the best cure for unhappiness, and Mrs. Frank's advice was to remember those who were even more unhappy. But to Anne, though no one listened to her, this could add only more misery to a cup already overflowing with it. "I simply can't build up my hopes on a foundation consisting of confusion, misery, and death. I see the world gradually being turned into a wilderness, I hear the ever approaching thunder, which will destroy us too, I can feel the sufferings of millions and yet, if I look up into the heavens, I think that this cruelty too will end, and that peace and tranquillity will return again." What she saw when she looked up was a reminder that despite all the ugliness inflicted on it, the world was still incredibly beautiful, and each time she could not get over the miracle of it. It was only from her very joy in being alive that she could draw her own sustenance, that and the sense of living things around her, first people—she was a city child and a gregarious one, and people were the nearest and dearest things to her heart—and then, like her lonely and exhausted flower girl and the terrified narrator of "Fear," from nature itself. Her own advice to those who suffered was: "Go outside, go to the fields, enjoy nature and the sunshine, go out and try to recapture happiness in yourself and in God." Unfortunately, she could not take her own advice literally, but she followed it as closely as she could. Peering through dirty net curtains and dusty windows, she marveled at the loveliness of the chestnut tree in the yard, thick with shiny green leaves, or on a cold winter morning climbed up to the attic where from her favorite spot on the floor she could catch a glimpse of the blue sky and of her beloved tree, now bare, "on whose branches little raindrops shine, appearing like silver, and at the seagulls and the other birds as they glide on the wind." Once, happening to be by an open window on a stormy evening, she was so spellbound by the beauty of the wind and rain that afterward she was willing to brave the dangers of a dark empty house—rats, burglars, raids—just to feel the night full on her face again. And these simple but piercing joys filled her with such gratitude and love that each night before she went to sleep, she prayed: "I thank you God, for all that is good and dear and beautiful."

Perhaps this was Anne's last prayer in hiding. Perhaps when she went to bed on the night of August 3, 1944, her last thought was of her own blessedness: her youth, her strength, her love for all the people and the growing things around her, her closeness to God, who had provided them. There is no way of knowing. On the next morning, the Dutch Nazi police suddenly stormed through the concealed doorway of the annex with drawn revolvers and took all its inhabitants away. In a heap of papers and books which the police had dumped on the floor during their search for money and valuables, Miep and Elli later found the notebooks Anne had kept so carefully. They put them aside for the day when Anne would come back for them, a time which never came.

Only Mr. Frank came back—by way of Odessa and Marseilles. He had been saved at the last only because he had been in the hospital at Auschwitz, and so had been alive when the Russians liberated the camp. Mrs. Frank died on January 6, 1945. She had begun to lose her mind in the days preceding her death; given some bread, she would hide it under the blanket, explaining that she was saving it for her husband, because he needed it. Margot died at the end of February or the beginning of March. She had been gravely ill, in a coma for days. While unconscious, she had fallen out of bed and was dead when her friends tried to lift her back. Anne, who was already sick with typhus at the time, was not informed of her sister's death, but (as related by a witness to Ernst Schnabel for his beautiful little book on Anne Frank) "she sensed it, and soon afterward she died, peacefully, feeling that nothing bad was happening to her." Mr. Van Daan was gassed; Otto Frank himself saw him taken to the gas chambers. Mrs. Van Daan died; no one knows how. Young Peter Van Daan was marched away from Auschwitz by S.S. battalions fleeing into Germany from the Russians and was never seen again. Mr. Dussel died in Neuengamme Camp. Of those who had looked after them all in the Secret Annex, and been taken to jail, all were eventually released, except Mr. Kraler; but he finally escaped and made his way back to Holland in time to see the liberation of the country from the Nazis.

Only the father returned—to learn that he alone was left and to be given his daughter's notebooks by Miep and Elli. The little books must have seemed pathetic enough to Otto Frank when, after his own slow recovery to health, he returned to Amsterdam to learn, after agonizing inquiries, that his wife and two children were dead. The diary was peculiarly heart-breaking, not only in its reminder of all that eight people had lived through and hoped for in more than two years of captivity, but in its revelation of Anne. Lies Goosens remembers Otto Frank's saying to her, when the *Diary* was first published: "Anne developed under our eyes in that room, but we went on treating her as though she still was a giddy little girl. All of us were too wrapped up in our own troubles to give her the understanding that she needed."

At first Mr. Frank had copies of the *Diary* privately circulated as a memorial to his family. It was a Dutch university professor who urged formal publication of the book, and with only very slight excisions by Mr. Frank, *Het Achterhuis* was published in Amsterdam by Contact Publishers, in June 1947. The book soon went through several editions. In 1950, it was published in Germany by the Heidelberg firm of Lambert Schneider. The first printing was 4,500 copies, and many booksellers were actually afraid to show it in their windows; but the book caught on rapidly, and the sales of the pocket edition, published by S. Fischer Verlag, total more than half a million. In 1950 it was published in France; in 1952, in England and the United States. By now the book has been translated into twenty-two languages, has been published in twenty countries, and has sold more than two and a half million copies. In the United States it had an enormous success in the Pocket Book edition and later was circulated by the Teen Age Book Club, the Book Find Club, and republished in the Modern Library. The book was serialized by an

American newspaper syndicate, with a calculated audience of ten million readers, and millions more read it when it was condensed in *Omnibook* and *Compact* magazines. A German translation of the book has been used in the United States as a school reader.

The book had a second life when it was dramatized by Frances Goodrich and Albert Hackett and became one of the most successful enterprises of the contemporary theater. In the United States the play won all the principal theater awards, and has since been produced in over twenty countries; it has now been made into a film, and soon the story of Anne Frank will have become perhaps the most celebrated document of a single human being's ordeal during World War II.

By now, in fact, Anne Frank has become a universal legend. Out of the millions who were gassed, burned, shot, hanged, starved, tortured, buried alive, the young girl who died so "peacefully" in Bergen-Belsen, almost in unconscious sympathy with her dead sister Margot, has become a prime symbol of the innocence of all those who died in the middle of the twentieth century at the hands of the most powerful state in western Europe. Perhaps more than any of the known dead, and certainly more than the now nameless ones who died scratching the ceilings of the gas chambers in the last agonized struggle against death, the girl born in Frankfurt of an upper-class Jewish family, whose father was a German officer in World War I, has become the personal example of the heartlessness, the bestiality, the still unbelievable cruelty of Germans in World War II. Upon her, at least, all agree; in her all peoples, in the uneasy peace since 1945 that is no peace, can find a moment's occasion for compassion and awareness. When *The Diary of Anne Frank* was produced on the Dutch stage, royalty wept; and by now, as everyone knows, Germans who had wept for no one but themselves, who had not allowed themselves to recognize the horror in their midst, who laughed in derision when they were made to see films of Auschwitz and Buchenwald, have wept in theaters over Anne Frank. In October 1956, when the play opened in seven German cities to silent audiences, there was by all accounts unexpected horror and dismay. Alfred Werner, in a study of "Germany's New Flagellants" (*The American Scholar*, Spring 1958), reports that not until 1956 was there a mass emotion of expiation in Germany, and that it started with the Hacketts' play. The play "broke through the tough shell that the German had grown around his soul. In what may be a natural drive for self-preservation, he had pushed all of the Nazi period into the remote corners of the subconscious mind. The victims who had lived through the Nazi era, or at least part of it, and visited Germany after 1945, knew all the time that this 'amnesia' of the Germans was only defense. But they also feared that this repression of a reality too painful to remember might eventually lead to an obliteration, to the myth that nothing had really happened between 1943 and 1945." Mr. Werner recalls Schiller's belief in the theater as a moral institution—"when a thousand burdens press upon our souls and the cares of our callings threaten to stifle our sensitivity, then, in such moods, the stage receives us: in this artificial world we dream the real one away . . ." but notes that to the Germans of 1956, *Das Tagebuch der Anne Frank* "meant something different . . . a much delayed rendezvous with fate." The critic of the *Frankfurter Allegemeine Zeitung* wrote:

There is no drama in the old sense. It belongs to the Passions of Christ, brought nearer to us step by step. Judging this play is beyond the capabilities of a German theater critic . . . Old wounds are broken open. The memory of shame and terror makes it almost impossible to subject this play to aesthetic rules of dramatic judgment, however broad they may be. . . . Those who feel guilty should feel it here most of all.

The German audiences who at the première of the play sat through it in perfect silence—"the packed auditoriums were frozen in silence when the curtain came down"—launched a mood of "repentance" and philo-Jewish enthusiasm which was a typically extremist German phenomenon. The programs requested "no applause," and night after night silent crowds filed out of the theaters. Television, radio, and press documented the fate of Anne Frank; teachers marched their classes to see the play; for the next few months, the *Diary* was the leading German best seller. The sympathy of German youth was such that on March 17, 1957, two thousand young people from Hamburg marched in the rain to the site of the former concentration camp at Bergen-Belsen where, in some unknown spot, Anne Frank lies buried. People traveled in trains, buses, on bicycles through the chilling rain to the low hilltop marked by a huge obelisk, a few gravestones, and the burial mounds. There were many speeches. One came from an ex-Nazi, Hans Hanoch Nissen, who was converted to Judaism, settled in Israel, and at the memorial meeting announced that "it was a great and comforting experience for me to see here the new German generation. I am united with you in the belief in a better future . . ."

The production of *Das Tagebuch der Anne Frank* coincided with what in certain intellectual circles became a pro-Jewish philosophy, a return to the abstraction of the "noble Jew" among the German intellectuals of the Enlightenment. It is for this reason that Anne Frank has symbolized so much—so peculiarly much—in current German thought. A sixteen-year-old girl, participant in the Belsen pilgrimage, wrote a letter published in newspapers all over the Bonn Republic: "I have sworn that we must do better! All must be made to realize that the highest and the most beautiful being is man—regardless of whether he is a Jew, a Dane, a Russian, an Englishman, a Frenchman, or a German. . . .

"Anne, you did not die in vain. We, today's youth, want to believe in what is good in man—as you did. . . . We shall never forget you and all those innocent people who had to die like you. We do not want to forget, and we must never forget."

This is the tone of many letters that have come to Otto Frank from Germans, the most significant of which are from young people. The typical mood is one of adolescent identification with Anne. A Berlin girl of sixteen: "I could not get along with my parents, which brought me almost to despair. Then I received the diary of your daughter Anne: 'I believe in the good which is in Men' is written there. This I had forgotten completely. . . ." Other letters suggest that to young people, German or non-German, the world just now can seem as frightening as it did to a Jew in hiding from the Nazis; at least they seem more vulnerable in these letters than their youth alone can explain. One girl began: "I am only 19 years of age." Another: "I am fifteen years old. This statement perhaps explains much to you. . . ." The naïveté of teen-agers sometimes becomes grotesque. A boy who read an article about the *Diary* in *Reader's Digest* asked: "Did your family ever see Hitler? If so, when? What were your impressions of Hitler and the Nazi way of life?" On the other hand, a sixteen-year-old Jewish girl affirmed: "I feel that God made Anne for a specific purpose. . . . She accomplished in death something that would have been practically impossible to do in life." For some Catholic girls, she has become a "saint." A girl from Boston wrote: "Anne's struggles for maturity have reminded me of mine, and yet she was so much more mature than I who am now sixteen."

So the flood of emotion, of repentance, of identification and commiseration streams in. The figure of universally accepted innocence, a young girl, is so perfect a subject that young people can identify with her; older people can pity her; the world can almost believe that it has made peace with itself over the unknown grave of Anne Frank. During the height of the German emotion over the play, reports Alfred Werner, a few Germans protested that "the play might be letting the Germans off too lightly, that it did not even begin to suggest how frightful were the German actions." Yet it is also a fact that it is impossible to make artistic use of the worst horrors of the concentration camps. *The Diary of Anne Frank* does not deal with horror—at least not directly; yet this, though it makes it too easy for all of us not to think of the horror at all, is also what makes both book and play *possible*. It was not only Germans who laughed derisively when shown the first films of the concentration camps; so did the English in Piccadilly newsreel theaters. The fact is that certain events in our time, prime and unforgettable images of human suffering and degradation, seem incredible to us even when we remember them, and are ungraspable even when we face them.

Anne Frank herself felt this about many horrors in her young life. She was in the Secret Annex, looking wistfully through a powerful pair of field glasses into the lighted rooms of the houses at the back: ". . . I never knew before that our neighbors could be such interesting people. . . . I found one

[13]

family having a meal, one family was in the act of taking a home movie; and the dentist opposite was just attending to an old lady, who was awfully scared." The day the Frank family was taken off to the German detention camp was a beautiful summer day. Anne's father told Ernst Schnabel, "As we rode toward Westerbork . . . Anne would not move from the window. Outside, it was summer. Meadows, stubble fields, and villages flew by. The telephone wires along the right of way curvetted up and down along the windows. It was like freedom." It must have seemed incredible to look at beautiful summer days, the peaceful summer scene, when she was in hiding because she was a Jew, or when she was in a train being led off to a concentration camp. It is this radical injustice, this unaccountability, that characterizes for children their most painful experiences; the anthropomorphic child in all of us can still feel the injustice of slipping out of life while someone else is yawning, or drinking beer. In the world of totalitarianism, the victim suffers from the illogic of his fate as well as the terror of death. But this incredibility is now what we feel about so many experiences in our time that it it no wonder that the most sensitive imaginations in Europe have committed themselves to a sense of the "absurd." It was "absurd" as well as unspeakable to put children into concentration camps; "absurd" as well as unforgivable to allow millions upon millions of innocent civilians, Jews and non-Jews, to die as they did. But absurd, out of focus, beyond the human scale, utterly illogical and often ungraspable as the death of an innocent fifteen-year-old girl at the hands of the Third Reich may be, it is a fact. It is a fact that never can be forgotten, that never will be forgotten. But it is also a fact that the reality of what certain people have had to endure in our time can be grasped humanly and politically only because of the modulation of a document like *The Diary of a Young Girl*, which permits us to see certain experiences in a frame, in a thoroughly human setting, so that we can bear them at all.

Anne Frank's Diary has rarely been subjected to criticism. The dramatic economy of the book has moved its readers just as much as the fate of its author has served as an occasion of emotion. Yet it has been suggested that Anne was unable to confront the hideousness of her experience, that her diary was an escape into the ideal. And in one sense this "evasion" of reality, if one may so call it, though improbable coming from people who have never had to face anything like Anne Frank's experience, is perfectly true. It may be that the "ideal" quality of the book accounts for the universal acceptance of the *Diary*; has made it possible for Germans to ease their souls sitting in a theater; for Jews to honor their dead; for the Dutch and the French to remember their suffering under the occupation; for adolescent children to take imaginative refuge from their problems. And yet it is a fact that Anne Frank's wholly domestic picture of life works toward the understanding of her true situation, rather than the other way around. For truthfully direct "war literature," naked shots of the ultimate horror, are hard for everyone to get down—this is as true for the victims' kin as it is for the Germans eager to evade responsibility; they stupefy instead of awakening us. The last shudder of death, the shriek of crucifixion—these really belong to death, not life. If we are still in danger of evading the full truth of Nazism, we are also in danger, when we think we are confronting the truth, of adding to the extreme abstractness and tension of the human spirit which represents Nazism, with its insatiable slogans and its monolithic sense of truth. The enemy of Nazism is its enemy because it is different from Nazism in kind, in intention, in the spirit with which it addresses itself to life. In the "ideal" world of Anne Frank's diary, in the preoccupation with potato peels, a young girl's discovery of puberty, there is the truth of life as human curiosity and sensitivity and fellowship—while outside, the green and gray German army lorries trundle past bearing their helpless Jewish victims to the slaughter heap.

The Diary of a Young Girl has survived its author and most of her family, as it has already survived so many books about the war, because the faithfulness with which it records an unusual experience reminds us—as opposition to Nazism on its own terms never can—of the sweetness and goodness that are possible in a world where a few souls still have good will. The *Diary* moves us because its author had the strength to see, to remember, to hope. There are scenes in the *Diary* of pure terror, and scenes that are sheer pantomimic farce out of a silent movie—Mrs. Van Daan being examined by the dentist, Mr. Dussel, writhes so miserably that his scraper gets caught in her mouth. "After much turning, kicking, screaming, and calling out, she got the instrument free at last and Mr. Dussel went on with his work as if nothing had happened!" There are scenes of wistful impressionism, "the blues." Anne, "sitting cozily" in the main office, looking out on the street through a slit in the curtain, writes to "Kitty": "It is dusk but still just light enough to write to you. It is a very queer sight, as I watch the people walking by; it looks just as if they are all in a terrible hurry and nearly trip over their own toes." She sees unattractive starved children in the neighborhood, "real slum kids with running noses . . ." and adds, "Other things to see—cars, boats, and rain. I like particularly the screech of the trams as they go by." She sees two Jews passing by. "I could hardly believe my eyes; it was a horrible feeling, just as if I'd betrayed them and was now watching them in their misery."

Yet the writer is inside, watching from her temporary nest, and the contrast with her daily experience and her future is in one sense frightful, in another her salvation. We can never fully know our own experience; the words that help us to bear them also separate us from the extremity of our living and our death. And since never as in our time have men had to bear so much, never have we felt so great a disproportion between words and reality. No wonder that we are so impatient with "art" when it claims some ultimate ordeal for its subject. But courage is always a single human being's courage, not the world's; it is the courage to face one's own experience and to remember the abyss that now lies on every hand. More than that cannot be asked of any human being. Anne Frank died of typhus in the hell of Bergen-Belsen. Yet when one weeps for her it is not out of pity. Pity is for the faceless and the weak. Events could only make Anne helpless. And though it is a miracle that her diary and her little stories and essays have survived at all, the real miracle is that in the young girl who wrote them life was so strong to begin with.

FABLES

Translated by Michel Mok

Kitty

KITTY IS the girl next door. In fair weather, I can watch her playing in the yard through our window. Kitty has a wine-red velvet frock for Sundays and a cotton one for every day; she has pale-blonde hair with tiny braids, and clear blue eyes.

Kitty has a sweet mother, but her father is dead. The mother is a laundress; sometimes she is gone during the day, cleaning other people's houses, and at night she does the wash for her customers.

Often she shakes out carpets late at night and hangs washing on the line. Kitty has six brothers and sisters. The smallest screams a lot and hangs on to the skirts of his eleven-year-old sister when mother says, "Children, it's bedtime!"

Kitty has a small cat which is so black that it looks like a Moor. She takes good care of the kitten, and every evening, before bedtime, you can hear her call, "Kitty, kitty, kitty!" That's how she came to be called Kitty, which may not be her name at all. She also has two rabbits, a white one and a brown one, that hop up and down in the grass.

Sometimes Kitty is naughty, just like other children. This happens mostly when she quarrels with her brothers. It's a sight to see her fight with them—she beats, kicks, and even bites them, and the little boys respect their sturdy sister.

"There are errands to be done!" Mother calls. Quickly Kitty sticks her fingers in her ears, so that she'll be able to say that she didn't hear her mother. Kitty hates running errands, but she wouldn't lie to escape it; Kitty doesn't lie; you need only to look into her blue eyes to know that.

One of Kitty's brothers is sixteen and works as an office boy. This brother sometimes bosses the other children as if he were their father. Kitty doesn't dare to contradict him, for she knows from experience that he is quick with his fists and also that he doesn't mind standing treat if one obeys him. Peter is generous and Kitty loves sweets.

Sundays, when the bell tolls, Kitty's mother and all the children go to church. Kitty prays for her dear father, who is in heaven, and also for her mother, that she may have a long, long life. After church they all go for a walk. Kitty enjoys this a lot; she is fond of wandering through the park, or better still, through the zoo. But that happens only in September, when it costs 25 cents.[1] Kitty's birthday is in September, and sometimes she asks for a trip to the zoo as a birthday gift. Other gifts her mother cannot afford.

Often Kitty comforts her mother who, after a day's hard

[1] The Amsterdam Zoological Society is a membership organization. In the month of September, the public is admitted to the park for 25 Dutch cents—roughly sixpence (ten American cents).—Translator.

work, weeps in the night. Then Kitty promises her all the things she, herself, would like to have when she is grown up. Kitty wants so badly to be grown up, earn money, buy pretty clothes, and treat her sisters to sweets, as Peter does. But before she can do all that, Kitty has to learn a lot and go to school for a long time.

Mother wants Kitty to go to Domestic Science School, but the girl doesn't care for that idea at all. She doesn't want a job in the house of some stuck-up lady. She wants to work in a factory, like those jolly chattering girls she sees passing by the window. In a factory you're never alone, you have company to gossip with. And Kitty loves gossiping. Once in a while she has to stand in the corner in school, because she talks too much.

Just the same, Kitty is fond of her teacher, who is sweet and terribly clever. How difficult it must be to study and get to know so much! But one can get along with less. Kitty's mother always says that a girl doesn't get a husband if she is too clever, and that, Kitty thinks, would be just awful. Later she would like to have dear little children, but not such children as her brothers and sisters. Kitty's children are going to be much prettier and sweeter. They will have curly brown hair instead of that straight flaxen stuff, and they will have no freckles, which Kitty has by the hundreds. Kitty doesn't want as many children as her mother has. Two or three would be enough, but, oh, it is so far, far off . . .

"Kitty!" her mother calls. "Come here. Where have you been, naughty girl? Just sitting there dreaming, I suppose. Quick, to bed with you!"

Kitty sighs. To be interrupted just as you are thinking of a glorious future!

Eve's Dream

"Good night, Eve, sleep well."

"Same to you, Mum."

Click went the light and Eve lay in the dark, but only for a few moments, because when she got used to the darkness, she saw that her mother had closed the curtains in such a way that an opening was left through which she could look straight into the face of the moon. The moon stood so quietly in the sky; he didn't move, smiled, and was friendly to everyone.

"If I could only be like that," Eve said softly to herself, "always quiet and kind so that everybody would like me. That would be wonderful."

Eve thought and thought about the difference between the moon and herself, who was still so very small. She finally dozed off, and her thoughts seemed to be transformed into a dream which Eve remembered so keenly next day that she afterwards sometimes wondered whether it had not actually happened.

[22]

She stood at the entrance of a big park, looking through the fence and not quite daring to go in. Just as she was about to turn back, a little girl with wings came up to her and said, "Go on, Eve, or don't you know the way?"

"No, I don't," said Eve shyly.

"Well, then, I will guide you." And with those words, the little elf took Eve's hand.

Eve had walked in several parks with her mother and her grandmother, but a park like this one she had never seen.

She saw a wealth of flowers, trees, fields, every imaginable kind of insect, and small animals such as squirrels and tortoises. The elf chatted gaily with her, and Eve had got over her fear enough to ask a question. But the elf stopped her by putting a finger to Eve's lips.

"I will show you and explain everything. After each explanation you may ask questions about things you don't understand, but otherwise you must be silent and not interrupt me. If you do, I shall take you home at once, and then you will know just as little as all the other stupid people.

"Well, now I begin: First of all, here is the rose, the queen of flowers. She is so beautiful and smells so wonderful that it goes to everybody's head, and most of all to her own.

"The rose is lovely, elegant, and fragrant, but if something doesn't please her, she immediately turns her thorns in your direction. She is like a spoiled little girl—very pretty and apparently quite sweet, too, but either touch her, or pay a little attention to somebody else, so that she is no longer the center of interest, and she shows her sharp nails. Her tone of voice becomes catty; she is offended but doesn't want to show it, and so her manners turn stilted and she puts on airs."

"But if all this is so, little elf, how is it that everybody considers the rose the queen of flowers?"

"It is because nearly all people are blinded by surface glitter; there are only a few who would not have voted for the rose if there had been an election. The rose is good-looking and dignified, and, just as in the rest of the world, scarcely anyone asks if there might not be another, outwardly a little plainer, perhaps, but inwardly more noble and gifted, for the role of ruler."

"But you yourself think the rose lovely, don't you, little elf?"

"Indeed, I do, and if she wouldn't always push herself into the foreground, she might be lovable as well. But since, by common consent, she is the flower of flowers, she will always regard herself as more beautiful than she really is, and so long as that is so, she will be full of false pride, I don't care for such creatures."

"Do you think that Lena, too, is full of false pride? She is also beautiful and, because she is rich, she is the head of the class."

"Think for a moment, Eve, and you will have to admit that, if little Marie, for example, had some complaint against Lena, Lena would turn the entire class against Marie. The reason? Simply that Marie is plain and poor. And you, all of you, would accept that false reason, because you know that if you did not, you would fall from Lena's good graces. And that, you think, is as bad as having the headmaster angry with you. You wouldn't be permitted to come to her beautiful home, and so you let her boss you. Later in life, such girls as Lena will stand alone, for the others, as they grow older, will understand how wrong she was. Rather than be lonely for ever, girls like Lena should change their ways."

"Do you think, then, elf, that I should try to convince the other girls not to listen to Lena?"

"Yes. First she will be furious with you. But later, as she gets more sense and realizes how badly she has acted, she will be graceful and have friends who are more sincere than those she has had until now . . ."

"I understand. But tell me, little elf, am I as full of false pride as the rose?"

"Listen, Eve: people and children who ask themselves such questions prove by that very act that they are free from false pride. You can best answer the question yourself, and I advise you to do so. . . . Now let us go on. Look at this: don't you think it is attractive?"

The elf knelt down by a small, blue, bell-shaped flower that waved back and forth in the grass to the rhythm of the wind.

"This little bell is kind, sweet, and simple. It brings joy to the world; it tolls for the other flowers just as a church bell tolls for people. It helps many flowers and comforts them. The little bell is never lonely, it has music in its small heart. This flower is much happier than the rose. It doesn't care about the praise of others. The rose lives only for and by admiration: if she doesn't get this, she has no other reason to be glad. Her outward splendor is for others; inside she is empty and, therefore, without happiness.

"The little bell, on the other hand, is not exactly beautiful, but it has genuine friends, who value its melodies; those friends live in its flower-heart."

"But the little bell is a pretty flower, too, isn't it?"

"Yes, but not as obviously as the rose. Unfortunately, it is this kind of 'show' that attracts most people."

"But I, too, often feel quite alone and like to have people about me. Is that not good?"

"That has nothing to do with it, Eve. Later, when you grow up, you, too, will hear the song in your heart; I am sure of it."

"Please, dear elf, go on with your story."

"All right, I will go on." The elf pointed upward with her small fingers. Eve looked at a huge, stately chestnut tree.

"This tree is impressive, isn't it?' asked the elf.

"Yes, it is grand; how old do you think it is?"

"It is surely more than a hundred and fifty years old, but it is still straight and doesn't feel old at all. Everybody admires this chestnut for his strength, and he proves that he knows his strength by his indifference to all this admiration. He doesn't tolerate anyone above himself and is egotistical in everything. So long as he lives, nothing else is of any importance. He looks as though he were generous and a support to others. But if you think that, you are mistaken. The chestnut is pleased when no one comes to him with troubles or complaints. He has a good life, but he begrudges it to everyone else. The trees and flowers know this. When they are in trouble, they go to the sympathetic pine and forget about the chestnut.

"Still, the chestnut, too, has a very small song in that big heart of his; you can tell that by his liking for the birds. For them he always has a little spot, and he often gives them a little something, though not much."

"Can the chestnut tree also be compared to some kind of person?"

"That, too, you need not ask, Eve. All living beings can be compared with each other, and the chestnut is no exception. He is not bad, you know, but neither is he good. He doesn't do anyone harm, lives his own life, and is satisfied. Any other questions, Eve?"

"No, I understand everything, and I am very grateful to you for your explanations, dear elf. Now I am going home. Will you come again sometime to tell me more?"

"That is not possible. Sleep well, Eve."

The elf was gone. Eve woke up; the sun had replaced the moon, and a cuckoo clock at the neighbors' called out seven.

The dream had made a big impression on Eve. Nearly every day she caught herself doing or saying little unpleasant things, which she then corrected at once according to the elf's good advice. She also tried hard not always to give in to Lena. But girls like that feel at once that someone is making an effort to "take them down a peg or two." She defended herself vigorously, especially when Eve proposed some game in which another girl would be the leader. Then Lena did everything she could to turn her faithful following against Eve.

Eve noticed with pleasure that Lena wasn't quite as smart in her dealings with her as she was with little Marie. As Marie was a small, slight, and shy girl, it amazed Eve that she dared to stand up against Lena. As she got to know her better, it became very clear to Eve that Marie, as a friend, was to be valued much above Lena.

Eve had told her mother nothing about the elf. She hardly knew why. Until now, she had confided in her mother, but for the first time she felt the need to keep something to herself. She didn't understand it, but she had a feeling that Mummy wouldn't be quite "with her" in this.

The little elf was so lovely, and Mummy had not been in the big park and hadn't seen the elf. Eve couldn't describe the elf's appearance. It wasn't long before the dream had such an influence on Eve that her mother noticed the change in her daughter. She talked about more interesting things than before and didn't get excited about trifles. But since Eve didn't speak of what had brought about the change, the mother didn't want to force herself into the child's confidence.

And so Eve lived on, thinking always of the elf's good counsel. She never saw the elf again. Lena no longer was the head of the class. The other girls now led the group by turns. At first, this had made Lena very cross, but when she found that angry words didn't help, she began to behave in a more friendly manner. Finally, her classmates, finding that she had outgrown her old faults, treated her like everyone else.

Eve decided to tell her mother of her experience. To her surprise, Mummy didn't laugh, but said: "That was a great privilege the elf gave you, Eve. I don't believe that she would think many children fit to receive it. Think always of the elf's trust in you, and don't talk about it to anyone. Do always what the elf told you, and don't get away from the path she showed you."

As Eve grew older, she became known for her good deeds. When she was sixteen, everyone in the community prized her as a kind, gentle, and helpful girl. Every time she did something good she felt warm and glad inside, and slowly she began to understand what the elf had meant by "the song in her heart."

When she was grown up, the solution of the dream and who and what the little elf had been suddenly came to her one day. She knew, as if in a flash, that it had been her own conscience which, in her dream, had shown her what was right. She was deeply thankful that, in her childhood, she had had the little elf as a guide and example.

Kathy

February 11th, 1944

KATHY SAT on the big boulder that lay in the sun in front of the farm. She was thinking, thinking very hard. Kathy was one of those quiet girls. What the youngster in the dirndl apron was thinking about, she alone knew; she never told her thoughts to anyone—she was much too withdrawn for that. She had no friends and probably would have found it hard to make any. Her mother found her a strange child, and the pity of it was that Kathy felt that. Her father, the farmer, was much too busy to concern himself with his only little daughter. And so Kathy was always by herself. It didn't disturb her; she didn't know any better and was soon satisfied.

But on this warm summer evening she sighed deeply as she looked up and glanced at the cornfields. How jolly it would be to play with those girls over there. Look, they ran about, and laughed; what fun they were having! Now the children came closer, and still closer—would they come to her? Oh, how awful, they came—but to laugh at her. She clearly heard them mention her name, not her real name, but the nickname that she hated so much and that she often heard the children whisper—Crazykate!

Oh, how miserable she felt; she could only run into the house, but if she did, the children would laugh at her all the more. Poor girl, it surely isn't the first time that you have felt so forsaken and envied the other youngsters . . .

"Kathy! Kathy, come home! We are having supper!" Another sigh, and the child slowly rose to obey her mother.

"My, what a cheerful face! We surely have a happy daughter!" the farmer's wife cried when the child, more slowly and more depressed than ever, entered the room. "Can't you say something for yourself?" scolded the woman. Her tone was more unfriendly than she herself knew; her daughter never had been the bright, lively girl she had always wanted.

"Yes, Mother," whispered the child.

"You're a fine one, staying away all morning and not doing a stroke of work. Where have you been?"

"Outside." Kathy felt as though she had a gag in her throat, but the mother misunderstood the girl's embarrassment and now really became curious as to where the child had been all morning. Again she asked:

"Answer me properly; I want to know where you have been, do you understand? I can't stand that everlasting, slow-witted, crazy behavior!"

At the word that reminded her of the detested nickname, Kathy lost control of herself and burst into tears.

"What is the matter now? You're a real coward! Can't you tell me where you've been? Or is that perhaps a big secret?"

The child could not possibly answer; violent sobs kept her from speaking. Suddenly, she upset a chair, ran weeping out of the room and up to the attic, where she sank down on some bags in a corner, sobbing as if her heart would break.

The mother shrugged her shoulders as she cleared the table downstairs; she wasn't surprised at her child's conduct. Such "crazy" moods were not unusual; she decided to let the girl alone—there was nothing to be gained, and the everlasting tears were always on the point of coming. A fine specimen of a twelve-year-old farmer's daughter!

In the attic, Kathy had calmed down somewhat and was collecting her thoughts. She would presently go downstairs, tell her mother that she had simply been sitting on the boulder by the door and thinking about things, and offer to finish all of the work that afternoon. Her mother then would surely understand that she did not mind the work, and should she be asked why she had been sitting still all morning, she would answer that there was something important she HAD to work out. Then, in the evening, when she had to deliver the eggs, she would buy a pretty, silver, glittering thimble for her mother; she had just enough money to buy one in the village.

Mother would realize that she wasn't so slow-witted and crazy, after all. Oh, if she could only get rid of that dreadful nickname! Here was a thought; if she had any money left over after buying the thimble, she'd get a bag of sweets and on her way to school, divide them among the girls. Then they'd like her and ask her to play with them. They would soon see that she was as good at games as anyone, and nobody would ever call her anything but Kathy after that.

Softly she descended the stairs. When she met her mother in the passage, all courage to talk and explain the morning's absence left her, and she quickly started cleaning the windows, one of her regular tasks.

It was almost sundown when Kathy took the basket of eggs and began her rounds. After a half hour's walk she reached the first customer, who stood in her doorway, dish in hand.

"I'll take ten tonight, my child," said the friendly woman.

She counted off ten and, with a greeting, continued on her way.

In three quarters of an hour the basket was empty, and Kathy stepped into the small general store. A pretty thimble and a bagful of sweets were soon put into the basket, and now Kathy turned back toward home. About half-way, she saw two of the girls who had teased her in the morning coming toward her. She bravely suppressed a longing to hide, and, her heart beating wildly, she went on.

"Look! Here comes Crazykate!"

At her wits' end, Kathy took the bag of sweets from her basket and politely held it out to the children. They quickly grabbed it from her and ran away with it. One of them stuck out her tongue at Kathy.

Lonely and heartbroken, Kathy sat down in the grass at the edge of the road, and wept, wept, and wept. Finally, in the dark, she dried her tears, picked up the basket, and slowly set off in the direction of home.

Somewhere in the grass, the thimble glittered . . .

The Flower Girl

February 20th, 1944

EVERY MORNING at seven-thirty the door of a little house at the edge of the village opens, and out steps a rather small girl, carrying a basket heaped with flowers on each arm. After shutting the door, she switches her burdens and starts the day's work. The people of the village, who answer her smiling nod as she passes, feel sorry for her. "That road is much too long and the job too hard," they think, "for a child of twelve."

But the little girl, herself, naturally doesn't know the thoughts of her fellow villagers. Merrily, and as quickly as her short legs will take her, she walks on and on and on. The road to the town is really very long; it takes her at least two and a half hours of steady walking to reach it and, with two heavy baskets, that's not easy.

When she finally trudges through the streets of the town she is exhausted, and it's only the prospect of soon being able to sit down and rest that sustains her. But the little one is brave and doesn't slow down her gait until she gets to her spot in the market. Then she sits down and waits and waits . . .

Sometimes she sits and waits all day because there are not enough people who want to buy something from the poor flower girl. Quite often Krista has to carry her baskets, still half full, back to the village in the evening.

But today things are different. It is Wednesday, and the market is unusually crowded and busy. Beside her, market women cry their wares, and all about her the little girl hears scolding and angry voices.

Passers-by can scarcely hear Krista, for her high little voice is almost drowned out in the market hubbub. But all day long, Krista doesn't stop calling, "Pretty flowers, sixpence a bunch! Buy my pretty flowers!" Some people who, finished with their errands, take time to look into the baskets, gladly pay a sixpence for one of the lovely small bouquets.

At twelve o'clock, Krista walks to the opposite side of the market square, where the owner of the coffee stand is in the habit of giving her, free of charge, a cupful with plenty of sugar. For this kind man Krista keeps her prettiest flowers.

Then she takes her seat again and once more starts crying her wares. At last, at half past three, she picks up her baskets and returns to the village. Now she walks much more slowly than she did in the morning. Krista is tired, terribly tired.

The trip back takes her a full three hours, and it is six-thirty when she reaches the door of the little old house. Inside everything is still the way she left it—cold, lonesome, and untidy. Her sister, with whom she shares the house, works in the village from early morning till late at night. Krista can't afford to rest; she is no sooner home than she begins to peel potatoes and clean vegetables. Her sister gets back from work at seven-thirty, and they finally sit down and have something to eat.

At eight in the evening the door of the cottage opens again, and once more the little girl comes out with the two big baskets on her arms. Now she walks into the fields that surround the little house. She doesn't have to go far; soon she bends down in the grass and picks flowers, all kinds of them, big ones and little ones, and all of them go into the baskets. The sun has almost set, and the child still sits in the grass, collecting her next day's supply.

The task is finished at last; the baskets are full. The sun has set, and Krista lies down in the grass, her hands folded under her head, and looks up into the sky.

This is her favorite time of day, and nobody need think that the hard-working little flower girl is dissatisfied. She never is and never will be so long as, every day, she may have this wonderful short rest.

In the field, amid the flowers, beneath the darkening sky, Krista is content. Gone is fatigue, gone is the market, gone are the people. The little girl dreams and thinks only of the bliss of having, each day, this short while alone with God and nature.

The Guardian Angel

February 22nd, 1944

ONCE UPON a time, an old lady and her young granddaughter lived for many years on the very edge of a large forest. The girl's parents had died when she was still quite small, and the grandmother had always taken good care of her. The little house in which they lived was a lonely place, but they didn't seem to realize it and were happy together.

One morning the old lady couldn't get up, because she was in great pain. Her granddaughter was now fourteen years old, and she looked after her grandma as well as she could. It lasted five days; then the grandmother died and the girl was all alone in the lonely cottage. As she knew hardly anyone and did not want to call in strangers to bury her grandmother, she dug a grave under an old tree in the woods, and there laid her grandma to rest.

When the poor girl came back to the house, she felt utterly forsaken and very sad. She lay down on her bed and cried her heart out. She lay there all day and didn't get up until evening, to get a bite to eat. So it went, day after day. The poor child no longer took pleasure in anything and only mourned for her dear old granny.

Then something happened that changed her entirely in just one day. It was night, and the girl was asleep when, suddenly, her grandmother stood before her. She was dressed in white from head to foot; her white hair hung down her shoulders, and she carried a small lamp.

From her bed, the girl watched her and waited for the grandmother to speak. "My dear little girl," the grandma began, "I have been watching you now every day for four weeks, and you never do anything but weep and sleep. That is not good, and I have come to tell you that you must work and spin; that you must take care of our little house and also dress prettily again.

"You mustn't think that, now I am dead, I no longer look after you; I am in heaven and always watch you from above. I have become your guardian angel, and I am always with you, just as before. Take up your work again, darling, and never forget that your granny is with you!"

Then granny disappeared, and the girl slept on.

Next morning when she awoke, she remembered what her grandmother had said, and she was filled with joy and no longer felt forsaken. She started working again, sold her spinning in the market, and followed her granny's advice at all times.

Later, much later, she also wasn't alone in the outside world. She was married to a fine man, a miller. She thanked her granny for not having left her alone, and she well knew that, though she now always had good company, her guardian angel would not leave her until the end of her days.

Fear

March 25th, 1944

IT WAS a terrible time through which I was living. The war raged about us, and nobody knew whether or not he would be alive the next hour. My parents, brothers, sisters, and I made our home in the city, but we expected that we either would be evacuated or have to escape in some other way. By day the sound of cannon and rifle shots was almost continuous, and the nights were mysteriously filled with sparks and sudden explosions that seemed to come from some unknown depth.

I cannot describe it; I don't remember that tumult quite clearly, but I do know that all day long I was in the grip of fear. My parents tried everything to calm me, but it didn't help. I felt nothing, nothing but fear; I could neither eat nor sleep—fear clawed at my mind and body and shook me. That lasted for about a week; then came an evening and night which I recall as though it had been yesterday.

At half past eight, when the shooting had somewhat died down, I lay in a sort of half doze on a sofa. Suddenly all of us were startled by two violent explosions. As though stuck with knives, we all jumped up and ran into the hall. Even Mother, usually so calm, looked pale. The explosions repeated themselves at pretty regular intervals. Then: a tremendous crash, the noise of much breaking glass, and an ear-splitting chorus of yelling and screaming. I put on what heavy clothes I could find in a hurry, threw some things into a rucksack, and ran. I ran as fast as I could, ran on and on to get away from the fiercely burning mass about me. Everywhere shouting people darted to and fro; the street was alight with a fearsome red glow.

I didn't think of my parents or of my brothers and sisters. I had thoughts only for myself and knew that I must rush, rush, rush! I didn't feel any fatigue; my fear was too strong. I didn't know that I had lost my rucksack. All I felt and knew was that I had to run.

I couldn't possibly say how long I ran on with the image of the burning houses, the desperate people and their distorted faces before me. Then I sensed that it had got more quiet. I looked around and, as if waking up from a nightmare, I saw that there was nothing or no one behind me. No fire, no bombs, no people. I looked a little more closely and found that I stood in a meadow. Above me the stars glistened and the moon shone; it was brilliant weather, crisp but not cold.

I didn't hear a sound. Exhausted, I sat down on the grass, then spread the blanket I had been carrying on my arm, and stretched out on it.

I looked up into the sky and realized that I was no longer afraid; on the contrary, I felt very peaceful inside. The funny thing was that I didn't think of my family, nor yearn for them; I yearned only for rest, and it wasn't long before I fell asleep there in the grass, under the sky.

When I woke up the sun was just rising. I immediately knew where I was; in the daylight I recognized the houses at the outskirts of our city. I rubbed my eyes and had a good look around. There was no one to be seen; the dandelions and the clover leaves in the grass were my only company. Lying back on the blanket for a while, I mused about what to do next. But my thoughts wandered off from the subject and returned to the wonderful feeling of the night before, when I sat in the grass and was no longer afraid.

Later I found my parents, and together we moved to another town. Now that the war is over, I know why my fear disappeared under the wide, wide heavens. When I was alone with nature, I realized—realized without actually knowing it—that fear is a sickness for which there is only one remedy. Anyone who is as afraid as I was then should look at nature and see that God is much closer than most people think.

Since that time I have never been afraid again, no matter how many bombs fell near me.

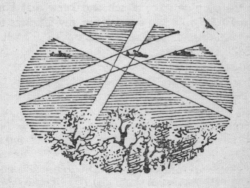

The Wise Old Dwarf

April 18th, 1944

THERE ONCE was a little elf called Dora. She was pretty and rich, and her parents spoiled her terribly. She was always laughing. She laughed from early morning until late at night; she was happy about everything and never gave sadness or sorrow a thought.

In the same forest where Dora made her home, there lived a dwarf by the name of Peldron. He was, in everything, the exact opposite of Dora. While Dora was for ever smiling at all the beauty and goodness about her, Peldron worried because there was so much misery in the world, and especially in the world of elves and dwarfs.

One day Dora had to do an errand at the shoemaker's in elves' village. And what do you think happened? She met that boring and long-faced Peldron. Dora was sweet but, because everyone liked her, she was a bit conceited, too. Boldly she ran toward Peldron, grabbed his pretty dwarf's hat and from a distance, laughed with the hat in her hands.

Peldron was really cross; he stamped on the ground and called, "Give me back my hat, give it back immediately!"

But Dora did no such thing, ran farther away, and finally

hid the hat in a hollow tree. Then she quickly continued on her way to the shoemaker.

After looking for it a long time, Peldron did find his hat. He couldn't take a joke, and especially not from Dora, whom he didn't like at all. Listlessly, he went on his way. Suddenly, a deep voice roused him from his brooding:

"Peldron, I am the oldest dwarf in the world, and also the poorest. Please, give me something, so that I may buy some food."

Peldron shook his head. "No. I won't give you anything," he said. "You had better die, so you needn't endure the misery of this world." And he hurried on without looking back.

Meanwhile, Dora, on her way back from the shoemaker, also met the old dwarf, and she, too, was asked for alms. Like Peldron, she refused, but for a different reason.

"I won't give you any money," she said. "If you are poor, it's your own fault. The world is so wonderful that I can't be bothered with poor people." And she skipped along.

With a sigh, the old dwarf sat down on a mossy spot, wondering what he should do with those two children. One was too sad, the other too gay, and neither would get very far in life that way.

Now, this ancient dwarf was no ordinary, everyday dwarf; he was a sorcerer, but not an evil one. On the contrary, he wanted people and elves and dwarfs to improve and the world to progress.

He sat there, thinking, for an hour. Then he rose and slowly walked to the house of Dora's parents.

The day after their meeting in the forest, Dora and Peldron found themselves locked up together in a small cabin. The old dwarf had taken them away to give them a proper training. The great sorcerer's wish was the same as a command, and even parents dared not disobey it.

What were those two to do in that hut? They weren't allowed to go out, nor were they permitted to quarrel. They had to work the whole day long! Those had been the old dwarf's orders. And so Dora worked, made jokes and laughed; and Peldron worked, looked gloomy and felt sad.

Every evening at seven, the old dwarf came to check on their work and then left again. They wondered how they could possibly get free. There was only one way, and that was to obey the old dwarf in everything.

You can't imagine how difficult it was for Dora to have to look at that long-jawed Peldron all day long; Peldron, Peldron, early and late, and never anybody else. But she hadn't much time to talk to him, anyway, even if she had wanted to, because she had to cook (she had learned that from her mother), keep the house clean and in order, and in her "spare time," if you please, get some spinning done.

Peldron, for his part, must chop wood in the enclosed garden, cultivate the grounds, and cobble shoes into the bargain. At seven in the evening, Dora called him to supper, and by that time they were both so tired that they could hardly talk to the old dwarf when he arrived on his nightly visit.

They kept this up for a week. Dora still laughed often, and yet she began to understand that there was a serious side to life. She realized that there were people who had a difficult time and that it was not asking too much to help such folk when they were in distress, instead of sending them away with some rude words. And Peldron lost a little of his gloom; it even happened, from time to time, that he whistled softly at his work, or grinned when he saw Dora laughing.

On Sunday they were both allowed to come with the old dwarf to chapel in elves' village. They paid more attention to the words of the dwarf-preacher than they had before, and they felt quite content as they walked back through the shady woods.

"Because you have been so good," said the old dwarf, "you may spend the day in the open, just as you used to do. But, mind you, tomorrow you go back to work. You can't go home, and you can't visit your friends."

Neither thought of running away; they were very glad to be permitted the freedom of the forest, even for one day. All that Sunday they played and had fun, watched the birds, the flowers and the blue sky, and enjoyed the warm sunshine. Happily, they returned to their cabin in the evening, slept until morning, and then went back to work.

The old dwarf made them lead this kind of life for four long months. Every Sunday morning they went to church, spent the rest of the day in the open, and worked hard the remainder of the week.

When the four months were up, the old dwarf one evening took both of them by the hand and walked into the woods with them.

"Look here, children," he said, "I am sure that you often have been angry with me. I also think that you both must be longing to go home."

"Yes," said Dora. And "Yes," echoed Peldron.

"But do you understand that this has been good for you?"

No, they didn't understand that very well.

"Well, I will explain it," said the old dwarf. "I took you here and left you together to teach you that there are other things in this world besides YOUR fun and YOUR gloom. You both will get along in life much better than before you came here. Little Dora has become somewhat more serious, and Peldron has cheered up a bit, because you were obliged to make the best of having to live together. I also believe that you like each other better than before. Don't you agree, Peldron?"

"Yes," said Peldron, "I like Dora much better now."

"Well," said the old dwarf, "you may go back to your parents. But think often about your stay in the little cabin. Enjoy all the fine things life will bring you, but don't forget the sorrows of others and try to comfort them. All people, children, dwarfs and elves can help one another.

"So, on your way, and don't be cross with me any more. I have done for you what I could, and it was for your own good. Good day, children, till we meet again!"

"Good-bye," said Dora and Peldron, and off they went to their homes.

Once more the old dwarf sat down in a shady spot. He had but one wish—that he might guide all the children of men into the right path, as he had guided those two.

And, truly, Dora and Peldron lived happily ever after! Once and for all they had learned the great lesson that people must laugh and weep, each at the right time. Later, much later, when they were grown up, they went to live together in a small house of their own free will, and Dora did the work inside and Peldron outside, just as they had when they were very young.

Blurry the Explorer

April 23rd, 1944

ONCE, when he was still very small, Blurry felt a great desire to escape from the fussing care of his mother bear and see something of the wide, wide world for himself. For days he was much less playful than usual, so busy was he thinking over his plans. But on the evening of the fourth day, his mind was made up. His plan was ready and only awaited execution. Early in the morning he would go into the garden—very softly, of course, so that Mimi, his little mistress, wouldn't notice—then he would creep through a hole in the hedge, and after that, well, after that, he would discover the world! He did all this, and so quietly that nobody knew he had escaped before he had been gone several hours.

As he crept out from under the hedge, his fur was smeared with earth and mud, but a bear who wants to make a voyage of discovery mustn't mind a little thing like a few spots of dirt on his skin. So, looking straight ahead, so as not to stumble over the uneven cobblestones, Blurry stepped smartly in the direction of the street, which could be reached through the alley between the gardens.

In the street he was a little frightened by the many grown-up people between whose legs he disappeared completely. "I must stay near the edge of the pavement," he told himself; "otherwise they'll run over me." And this was, indeed, the most sensible thing to do. Yes, Blurry was intelligent, which was self-evident because, tiny as he was, he wanted to see the world.

He kept close to the edge and saw to it that he wasn't caught between a pair of big, fast-moving feet. But suddenly his heart started pounding as if he had sledgehammers inside his chest. . . . What was that? A big black abyss lay before his feet. It was an open cellar, but Blurry didn't know that, and he got dizzy. Must he go down in there? Terrified, he looked about, but the trousered men's legs and the skirted ladies' legs calmly walked around the gaping hole and acted as if nothing were amiss. Not quite recovered from the shock, step by little step, he followed their example, and it wasn't long before he could continue.

"Now I'm walking in the big world," thought Blurry, "but where is the world? Because of all those trousers, skirts, and stockings, I cannot see the world at all. Perhaps I am too small to discover the world, but that doesn't matter. If I eat my porridge and swallow my cod-liver oil every day (he shuddered at the idea), I will get just as big as those people. Let's go on; sooner or later, in one way or another, I'll see the world."

He walked farther and paid as little attention as possible to the many fat and thin, long and short legs around him. But must he just walk and walk and walk? He was getting hungry and it was also beginning to grow a bit dark. Blurry had not given eating and sleeping any thought. He had been too much occupied with his plans of discovery to think of such ordinary and unheroic things as eating and sleeping.

Sighing, he walked on for a while until he discovered an open door. He hesitated on the threshold and then quietly went in. He was in luck, for, after passing through another door, he saw two saucers standing on the floor between some wooden legs. One of the saucers was filled with milk; the other with some sort of food. Starving, Blurry drank every drop of the milk. Then he ate the delicious food in the other saucer and felt entirely satisfied.

But, oh, what was THAT? Something white with green eyes approached slowly, staring at him. Directly in front of him, it stopped and asked in a strange small voice:

"Who are you, and why have you eaten all my food?"

"I am Blurry, and, on a voyage of discovery, a fellow needs something to eat. But I really didn't know that it belonged to you."

"So, you are on a voyage of discovery. But how is it that you had to discover just MY saucer?"

"Because I didn't see any other," Blurry answered in an unfriendly tone. Then he thought better of it, and asked in a kindlier manner:

"But what is your name, and what kind of strange creature are you?"

"I am Muriel and I belong to the family of Angora cats. I am very valuable, at least my mistress always says so. But you know, Blurry, I am always alone and am often bored. Won't you stay with me for a while?"

"I will stay and sleep here," said Blurry as though he were doing Muriel a favor. "But tomorrow, I must go on and discover the world."

As a beginning, this seemed fair enough to Muriel.

"Come along," she said, and Blurry followed her to another room where he again saw nothing but wooden legs. Still there was something else. In a corner stood a big wicker basket in which lay a pillow covered with green silk. Muriel stepped on to the pillow with her dirty feet, but Blurry thought it a pity to soil things that way. "Shan't I first clean up a bit?" he asked. "I'll wash you, just as I wash myself," replied Muriel. Blurry was not acquainted with that method,

and that was a good thing, for had he known he wouldn't have permitted Muriel to start.

Now the cat told him to stand up straight and calmly ran her tongue over his feet. It made Blurry shiver and he asked if that was her usual way of taking and giving baths.

"Yes, it is," she said. "You will see how clean you'll get; you will shine, and a shiny bear has the entrée everywhere and so finds it much easier to discover the world." Blurry controlled his shivers and uttered no complaint, brave bear. Muriel's bath seemed to take hours; Blurry was getting a little impatient, and his feet hurt from standing so long, but finally he did shine. Muriel again stepped into the basket and Blurry, who was exhausted, lay down. In less than five minutes they were both asleep.

Next morning Blurry awoke, and it took him a while to realize where he was. Muriel snored a little, and Blurry badly wanted his breakfast. Without considering the comfort of his hostess, he shook her and started to give her orders:

"Give me my breakfast, please, Muriel; I am awfully hungry."

The pretty Angora puss first had a good yawn, stretched to twice her usual length, and answered:

"No, no, you get nothing more. My lady musn't notice that you are here; you must leave, as quickly as possible, through the garden."

Muriel jumped out of the basket, took Blurry along through the room, out of the door, into another door, and then again out of a door, this time a glass one, and they were outside. "Bon voyage, Blurry," she said. "Till we meet again!" And she was gone.

Lonely and no longer convinced of his cleverness, Blurry walked through the garden and then, through the hole in the hedge, into the street. Where should he go, and how long would it take to discover the world? Blurry didn't know. Very slowly he walked along when suddenly a big four-legged thing ran toward him at full speed. It made tremendous noises so that Blurry, almost deafened and shaking with fear, clung to the side of a house. The gigantic thing halted, and Blurry began to cry from fear. The monster, not a bit disturbed by this, sat down and did nothing but stare at the poor little bear with his big eyes. Blurry pulled himself together. "What do you want of me?" he asked.

"I only want to take a look at you, because I've never seen anything like you."

Blurry breathed a sigh of relief. After all, one could talk, even with this ogre. Here was a curious thing, Blurry thought; why couldn't his own little mistress ever understand him? But he didn't have much time to consider this weighty question, for the big beast opened his mouth wide, showing all his huge cruel teeth. This made Blurry shiver worse than he had during Muriel's washing session. What would the monster do to him? He soon found out, for the beast, without a by-your-leave or with-your-leave, grabbed him by the neck and dragged him through the street.

Blurry couldn't cry, for he would have choked to death if he had; shouting was also out of the question. All that was left him was to shudder, and that didn't give a fellow any courage. He didn't have to walk now; if his neck hadn't hurt so, it wouldn't have been too bad; it was like a ride.

After all, it could be worse. But you did get woozy in the head from that continuous pushing. Where, where, is he taking me? Where? . . . Blurry, held fast by the animal, had dozed off. But the nap didn't last long. The beast suddenly was at a loss to know why he carried this thing in his teeth. Carelessly, he dropped him and ran off. And there lay the helpless little bear who wanted to discover the world, all alone with his pain. Bravely, he rose in order not to be tramped upon, rubbed his eyes, and looked around.

Far fewer legs, far fewer people, much more sun, and fewer cobbles under his feet. Could this be the world? There was no room in his poor head for thoughts; everything hurt and hammered in there. He didn't want to walk any more. Why should he? Muriel was far away, his mother still farther, and his little mistress . . . No! He was on his way, and he must persist until he had discovered the world.

A sound behind him startled him, and he turned around, hoping that no other beast was going to bite him. No, it was a little girl.

"Look, Mama, a little bear! May I take him along?"

"No, my dear, he is sick. Look, he is bleeding."

"That doesn't matter, Mama; we can wash it off when we get home. Then I'll have something to play with."

Blurry didn't understand a word of this conversation; little bears know only animal talk. But the little blonde girl looked so sweet that he didn't resist when he was wrapped in a scarf and put into a bag.

So, swaying to and fro, Blurry continued his voyage through the world. After they had walked for a time, Blurry, with the scarf still around him, was taken out of the bag, and the girl carried him on her arm. That was a piece of luck, for now he could see the road from above. What big piles of stones, very high, with here and there a white opening! And, way up on top, almost to the sky, there was a swirl of smoke. That must be for decoration, just like the feather on his little mistress's hat. Wasn't that funny?

Below, on the road, something said "toot-toot" and ran very fast, though it had no legs, only some round, blown-up things. Say what you like, it was worth the trouble to go and discover the world? What was the use of always staying at home? Why were you born? Surely not to stay for ever with your mother. No, see and experience things, that was the way to grow up! Yes, Blurry knew what he wanted.

At long last the girl stopped at a door. She went in, and the first thing Blurry saw was something on the order of Muriel. This one was called Puss, if Blurry remembered right. This Puss stroked the legs of the blonde girl, but she pushed him away and took Blurry to a white thing. It was high above the ground, wide and smooth. At the side, there was something of shiny metal which could be turned. This the blonde girl did, and she set him down on a hard, cold place. Then the girl began to wash him, especially that part of his fur where that nasty beast had bitten him. It hurt a lot and Blurry cried, but no one seemed to mind.

Fortunately, this wash didn't last as long as the one Muriel had given him, but it was colder and much wetter. The girl finished her task pretty quickly, dried him, wrapped him in a fresh scarf, and put him in a down bed, just like the one his little mistress had for him. But why go to bed? Blurry wasn't the least bit tired and didn't want to go to sleep. The girl was no sooner out the room than he slid out of bed and by way of a large number of doors and holes, landed once more in the street.

"I must get something to eat," thought Blurry. He sniffed; "Yes, there ought to be something good around here, for you can smell it."

He followed his nose and soon stood at the door from which the fine aroma came. He slipped into the big shop between the stockinged legs of a lady. Behind a big high something stood two girls. They quickly caught sight of him. They must have worked hard all day long and would like a little help, for they picked him up at once and placed him in a rather dark space where it was very, very hot.

That wasn't so bad; the main thing was that you could eat there as much as you pleased. On the floor and on low shelves, there lay rows of buns, rolls, and pastries, prettier than any Blurry had ever seen. What, after all, HAD Blurry seen? Not so much, come to think of it. Hungrily, he attacked the good things and ate so much that he was almost sick.

Then he took another thorough look round. There was really much to be seen here, it looked like a sweet-tooth's paradise. Everywhere loaves of bread, rolls, tarts, biscuits just for the taking!

And it was very busy here. Blurry saw many white legs, very different from those in the street. But there wasn't much time for dreaming; the girls, who had been standing at a little distance, pushed a broom into his hands and showed him how to use it. Sweep the floor—Blurry knew all about it—he had seen his mother do it. But it wasn't as easy as it looked. He tried bravely, but the broom was big and heavy, and the dust tickled his nose so that he had to sneeze.

And it was so hot; he felt more and more uncomfortable from the work he wasn't used to and the heat, but each time he stopped to rest for a minute, somebody put him back to work and gave him a slap besides.

"If only I hadn't walked in here so hastily," he thought, "then I would have been spared all this heavy work." But there was nothing he could do about it. He had to sweep, and sweep he did. When he had swept a long time, so long that the dirt lay in a big heap in a corner, one of the girls took him by the hand and led him to a spot where some hard yellow shavings lay on the floor. They told him to lie down, and Blurry understood that he was allowed to sleep.

He stretched out as if the shavings were a comfortable bed, and he slept until the next morning. At seven o'clock he had to get up, was again permitted to eat all he wanted, and once more was put to work. Poor Blurry, he wasn't even rested. He wasn't used to working and the heat bothered him terribly. His little head, arms, and legs ached, and he felt as if every part of him was swollen.

Now for the first time, he began to long for home, for his mother, his little mistress, his soft bed, and the nice lazy life; but how would he ever get there? Escape was out of the question; they kept a sharp eye on him and, besides, the only door to the street was in the room where the two girls worked all day long. No, Blurry simply had to bide his time. His thoughts were confused, he felt dizzy and weak. Everything about him started to turn; he sat down—nobody told him not to. When he felt a little better, he went back to work.

After a week of sweeping from morning until evening, he scarcely knew anything else. Little bears forget quickly, and that is a good thing. But he had not forgotten his mother and his home; only they seemed so unreal and so very far away!

One evening the two girls who had caught Blurry read this advertisement in the newspaper:

> REWARD FOR THE RETURN OF A SMALL BROWN BEAR
> WHO ANSWERS TO THE NAME OF BLURRY

"Do you think that could be our little bear?" they asked each other. "He doesn't work very hard; in fact, you can't expect it from such a small creature. If we get a reward for returning him, we will be better off than we are now."

They ran to the back of the shop and yelled, "Blurry!"

Blurry looked up from his work; had anyone called him? The big broom fell from his hands; how did they know his name? The girls came closer, and once more they called, "Blurry!"

He ran toward them. "Yes, his name is Blurry, all right," one of the girls said to the other. "Let us take him back tonight."

That same evening, Blurry was delivered to the home of his little mistress, and the girls got their reward. Blurry's little mistress gave him a spanking for his disobedience, and then a kiss because he was safely home again. His mother only asked:

"Blurry, why did you run away?"

"I wanted to discover the world," was his answer.

"And did you discover it?"

"Oh, I have seen very, very much. I have become a very experienced bear."

"Yes, I know all that; but I asked you if you had discovered the world."

"No, no . . . not really; you see, I couldn't find it!"

bij het ene meisje tegen het andere. "Laten we hem van=
avond nog eens gaan hengen." Dat was goed. En nog
diezelfde avond werd Bluey aan het lijn van zijn bekwaam=
nelst afgezogen en kregen de meisjes hem kleinig.

Jan: Als het daarnaast hele Blueg een pak slag door de
ongelook = ... heid en toen zei Jan omdat hij twee hoog
ziet. Jan zijn moeder hele hij alleen maar het volgende
de doen:
"Blueg waarom ben je weggelopen?"
"Ik wou de wereld ontdekken," antwoordde Blueg.
"En heb jij hem ontdekt?"
"O, ik heb heel, heel veel gezien, ik ben een zeer ervaren
... geworden!"
"Ja dat weet ik, maar ik vraag of je de wereld ont=
dekt hebt?"
"Nee...... ik ...... dat eigenlijk niet, ik kon de wereld
niet vinden!"

———————————————————————

De fee

De fee, die ik bedoel was geen gewone fee, zoals er zovele
... vinden zijn in sprookjesland. Nee, misschien was een
heel bijzondere fee. Bijzonder in haar uiterlijk en
bijzonder in haar manier van doen. Waarom, zul me
jullie=lees vragen was die fee dan zo bijzonder?
Wel, omdat zij niet heel ... hield en daar wat spel
maakte, maar omdat zij het zich tot taak had ge=
steld veelte en menzen te ... lijden.
Die bijzondere fee heette Ellen. Haar ouders waren ge=
storven toen zij nog maar heel klein was, maar
hadden haar veel geld nagelaten. Ellen kon zich al als
klein meisje alles doen wat zij zo lang en alles
kopen wat zij graag wilde hebben. Andere kinderen,
zoals of Alfje zouden daardoor ... geworden
zijn, maar haar Ellen altijd el ze bijzonder was,
werd zij helemaal niet bedorven!
Toen zij ouder werd had zij nog steeds veel geld, en
dat kleinde menzen anders die dan om straatie
alleen de kopen en delen te eten.
Op elze morgen werd Ellen wakker en bemijl zij nog
in haar zachte bedje lag, dacht zij hoeveel van het
moet al dat geld! Ik begonnen." voor mijzelf kan
ik het toch niet allemaal gebruiken en in mijn

The Fairy

May 12th, 1944

THE FAIRY I am talking about was no ordinary fairy of whom you find so many in fairyland. Oh, no, my fairy was a very special fairy, special in her appearance and special in her way of doing things. Why, everybody is sure to ask, was that fairy so special?

Well, because she didn't just help somebody here, and make some fun there, but because she had set herself the task of bringing happiness to the world and to all people.

This special fairy was called Ellen. Her parents had died when she was still quite little and had left her money. So Ellen could do as she chose and buy everything she wanted, even as a small girl. Other children, fairies and elves would get spoiled in that way, but not Ellen. As she grew older, she spent her money only to buy pretty clothes and delicious things to eat.

One morning Ellen lay awake in her soft bed, wondering what to do with all her money. "I can't use it all myself," she thought, "and I can't take it with me into the grave. Why shouldn't I use it to make others happy?"

That was a good plan, and Ellen wanted to carry it out at

[54]

once. She rose, dressed, took a small wicker basket, put into it part of one of her bundles of money, and went out.

"Where shall I begin?" she asked herself. "I know. The widow of the wood chopper is sure to be pleased with a visit of mine. Her husband has just died, and the poor lady must be having a difficult time."

Singing, Ellen walked through the grass and knocked at the door of the wood chopper's cottage. "Enter!" came a voice from the inside. Ellen softly opened the door and looked into a darkened room. In a far corner a little old woman sat knitting in a shabby armchair.

She was surprised as Ellen entered and immediately laid a handful of money on the table. Like everybody else, the woman knew that one must not refuse the gifts of fairies and elves.

"That is very sweet of you, little one," she said. "There are not many people who make gifts without expecting something in return, but happily the folk of fairyland are an exception."

Ellen looked at her in amazement. "What did you mean by that?" she asked.

"I simply meant that there are few who give and don't want something back."

"Is that so? But why should I want something from you? I am glad that my basket is a little lighter."

"Good!" said the old lady. "Thank you very much."

Ellen bade her good-bye and left. In ten minutes, she had reached the next cottage. Here she also knocked, though she didn't know the people. She hadn't been there long before she understood that money was not a problem here. The people did not lack *things*—they were poor in happiness. The lady of the house received her kindly, but she seemed to have no sparkle; her eyes were dull and she looked sad. Ellen decided to remain here a little longer.

"Perhaps I can help this lady in some other way," she thought, and really, when the sweet little fairy had seated herself upon a cushion, the woman began to talk about her troubles without being asked.

She spoke of her wicked husband, of her naughty children, and all her other misfortunes. Ellen listened, put in a question now and then, and became much concerned about the woman's sorrow.

When the woman had finished her story, Ellen spoke.

"Dear lady," she said, "I don't know about such things from experience, I'd like to give you some advice, which I, myself, always follow when I feel lonely and sad.

"One fine morning, take a walk through the big forest until you reach the moor. Then, after walking for a while in the heather, sit down somewhere and do nothing. Only look at the blue sky and the trees, and you will gradually feel peaceful inside and realize that nothing is so hopelessly bad that something can't be done to improve it—even a little."

"No," said the lady. "That remedy will help just as much as all the other pills I have swallowed."

"Try it, anyway," urged the fairy. "Alone with nature, all worries leave you. You grow first quiet, then glad, and feel that God has not deserted you."

"If it will please you," said the woman, "I will try it one day."

"Good. If I may, I will drop in again next week at this time."

And so Ellen went from house to house, cheering and comforting people, and at the end of the long day her basket was empty and her heart full; she knew that she had put her money to better use than by buying clothes. From that day on, Ellen often went on her rounds. She wore her yellow flowered frock, her hair was tied with a big bow, and she carried her basket on her arm. That's how she looked when she made her visits.

Even the woman who had enough money but too much trouble was beginning to feel happier. Ellen knew it; her remedy always worked.

The fairy gained many friends—not other fairies and elves, but people and children. The children told her everything, and this gave her much insight and the ability to have the right word of comfort on every occasion.

But so far as her money was concerned, she had miscalculated. After about a year, she had just enough left to live on.

Now, whoever thinks that this made Ellen sad and kept her from offering gifts is mistaken. She continued to give much; not money, but good advice and loving, healing words. She had learned that, even if one is all alone, one can still make one's life beautiful; and no matter how poor one is, one can still give others riches.

When Ellen died, a very old fairy, there was more mourning in the land than there had ever been before. But Ellen's spirit was not gone. When people slept, she returned to give them blissful dreams; even in their slumber they received the gift of wise counsel from this very special fairy.

Rita

IT WAS a quarter past four, and I was walking through a rather quiet street. I had just decided to drop in at the nearest pastry shop when, from a side street, there came a couple of teen-aged girls who, chatting busily, walked arm-in-arm in the direction I had chosen.

From time to time it is interesting and refreshing to listen to the conversation of teen-aged girls, not only because they laugh at the merest trifle, but also because their laughter is so infectious that everyone in their vicinity must involuntarily laugh with them.

So I walked stealthily behind the pair and eavesdropped on their talk, which had to do with the spending of their pocket-money. They consulted each other seriously on what to get for their money, and one could tell that their mouths watered at the thought of it. At the pastry shop, they continued their chat while looking at the wares in the show window.

As I, too, was fairly eating the delicious things with my eyes, I knew what their choice would be before they stepped into the shop. Inside it wasn't busy, and the girls were served at once. They had picked two fruit tarts which, wonder above wonder, they managed to take, untouched, out of the shop.

A minute later I also was ready, and once more the two walked, talking loudly, ahead of me. On the next corner there was another pastry shop, in front of whose window there stood a little girl, taking in the display with greedy eyes. Soon the three were talking together, and I reached the corner in time to hear one of the teenagers ask:

"Are you hungry, little one? Would you like a fruit tart?" The tiny one, of course, said, "Yes."

"Don't be foolish, Rita," said the other teenager. "Put your tart quickly into your mouth, as I did, for if you give it to this kid, you'll have nothing."

Rita didn't answer but stood there undecided for a moment, looking from the tart to the little girl and back again. Then she suddenly gave the child the pastry and said:

"Please, eat this, my dear; I'm going home to dinner, anyway."

And before the little one could thank her, Rita and her friend had disappeared. As I passed the youngster, who had taken a big bite from the tart with obvious relish, she offered it to me.

"Have a taste, miss; I got this for a present."

I thanked her and, smiling, I walked on. Who do you think got the most pleasure from the fruit tart—Rita, her friend, or the little girl?

I think it was Rita.

PERSONAL REMINISCENCES AND SHORT STORIES

Translated by Michel Mok

Do You Remember?

July 7th, 1943

Do you remember? I spend happy hours talking about school,
the teachers, our adventures, and—boys. When we still were
part of ordinary, everyday life, everything was marvelous. That
one year in the Lyceum was sheer bliss for me; the teachers,
all they taught me, the jokes, the prestige, the romances, and
the adoring boys.

Do you remember the day I came home, and there was a
package in the letter-box, marked "D'un ami—R."? It couldn't
have come from anyone but Rob. Wrapped in the little
parcel was a brooch worth at least two-and-one-half guilders,[1]
and ultra-modern. Rob's father dealt in such things. I wore
it two days, and then it broke.

Do you remember how Lies and I betrayed the class? We
had a French test. I was pretty well prepared, but not Lies.
She copied everything from me and I peeked at her work—
to improve it! Though Lies's paper was a trifle better than
mine, probably through the help I had given her, the teacher
decided to give us both a big fat zero. Great indignation! We
went to the headmaster to complain and set things straight.
At the end of the conference, Lies blurted out, "But, mind
you, Sir, the entire class had open books under the desks!"

[1] About five shillings (approximately seventy American cents).

[63]

The head promised not to punish the class, provided that all who had copied their work would raise their hands when asked about it. Ten hands, not even half the true number, went up. A day or two later, we were unexpectedly given the French test all over again. Lies and I were "cut dead" as traitors. Pretty soon I found myself unable to endure this treatment, and I wrote a long, pleading letter to Class 16 II, begging forgiveness. In two weeks, the whole thing was forgotten.

The letter was roughly as follows:

To the pupils of Class 16 II,

Anne Frank and Lies Goosens herewith offer the pupils of Class 16 II their sincere apologies for the cowardly betrayal in connection with the French test.

It was an unpremeditated, thoughtless act, and we admit without hesitation that we are the only ones who should have been punished. We think that anyone, in anger, might let a word or sentence slip that carries unpleasant consequences, but that was never intended to cause any harm. We hope that 16 II will regard the incident in that light and repay evil with good. Nothing can be done about it, and the two guilty ones can't undo their misdeed.

We wouldn't write this letter if we were not genuinely sorry. We ask those who have "cut" us until now to reconsider, for after all, our act was not so heinous that we have to be looked upon as criminals for all eternity. We beg those who cannot get over our mistake to give us a thorough scolding or, if they prefer, ask us to perform some service which, if at all possible, we shall carry out.

We trust that all of the pupils in Class 16 II will forget the affair.

Anne Frank and
Lies Goosens

Do you remember how Pim told Rob in the tram that Anne was much prettier than Denise, especially when she smiled, and how Sanne, who was also a passenger, overheard this and repeated it to me? And that Rob answered, "Your nostrils are much too wide, Pim!"

Do you remember that Maurice wanted to call on Father to ask him if he could keep company with his daughter?

Do you remember that Rob and Anne Frank carried on a busy correspondence while Rob was sick in the hospital?

Do you remember how Sam pursued me on his bike and wanted to ride hand-in-hand with me?

Do you remember how Bram kissed me on the cheek when I gave him my solemn promise not to tell a soul about the goings on between him and Suzy?

Oh how I wish that those happy, carefree days could come again!

My First Day at the Lyceum

August 11th, 1943

WITH a lot of fuss, talk, and planning, things were finally fixed so that I could register at the Lyceum and—without an entrance exam! I was a poor student in every subject, but particularly in maths, and I trembled as I thought of the geometry course that stared me in the face.

At the end of September, the post brought the long-awaited letter announcing the date in October on which I was to report at the Lyceum. That day it rained cats and dogs, and it was impossible to go by bike. So I used the tram, together with plenty of others.

There was a big crowd at the school; groups of boys and girls stood about, chatting; some walked from one group to another, recognizing friends and acquaintances, and asking, "Which class are you in?"

Aside from Lies Goosens, I hadn't discovered a single person I knew who would become a class-mate, and that situation didn't strike me as being very pleasant. The school doors opened, and in our class-room we were welcomed by a grey teacher with a mouse-face, who wore a long dress and flat-heeled shoes.

She stood there rubbing her hands as she watched the hub-bub in front of her and made the usual announcements. The teacher called and checked the names of the students, told us what books had to be ordered, and discussed some other details. Then we were dismissed and could go home again.

To tell the truth, I was deeply disappointed; I had expected at least to see the schedule and—to meet the Headmaster. I did see, in one of the halls, a jolly, fat little man with red cheeks, who, smiling at everyone who passed, stood talking with another chap of the same height, who was thin, had a dignified face and silky hair, and wore spectacles. But I had no idea that the fat man was the building superintendent, and the thin one the Headmaster.

Back home I gave an excited report of my experiences, but, to be honest, I knew as much of the school, the teachers, the children, and the schedule as I did before I left.

School started a week later. Again the rain came down in buckets, but I insisted on going by bike. Mother packed a cover-all in my schoolbag so that, in heaven's name, I shouldn't get drenched, and off I went.

Margot rides her bike at a furious clip, and in a couple of minutes I was so out of breath that I begged her to slow down a little. Another few minutes and the heavy rain changed into a regular cloudburst. Mindful of Mother's cover-all, I stopped and, with much difficulty, put on that unflattering garment. I remounted my bike, but soon the pace proved too fast for me again, and once more I asked Margot to take it easy. Very much out of sorts, she said that in the future she'd prefer to ride by herself; no doubt she was afraid of being late. But we reached the school with time to spare and, after parking the bikes, we stood chatting for a while in the shelter of the arcade that leads to the Amstel River.

We entered school on the dot of eight-thirty. Just inside the entrance there was a big sign announcing that about twenty students had to change class-rooms. I was included, and I was told to move to Class 16 II. This meant that I would belong to a group in which I knew a few boys and girls, but Lies was to remain in 12 I.

When I was given the desk at the very bottom of the class, behind girls much bigger than myself, I felt lonely and forsaken. In the second hour I raised my hand and asked to be moved to another spot, as I could see very little unless I fairly hung into the aisle.

My request was granted immediately, and I picked up my things and moved. The third hour was gym, and the teacher seemed so nice that I asked her to try to have Lies transferred to my room. How the dear lady did it I will never know, but the next hour, in walked Lies and was given the desk beside mine.

Now I was reconciled to the school—the school where I was to have so much fun and learn such a lot. Full of courage, I paid close attention to what the geography master was telling us.

A Lecture in Biology

August 11th, 1943

RUBBING HER hands, she walks into the room; rubbing her hands, she sits down; rubbing her hands, rubbing her hands, rubbing her hands.

Miss Riegel of Biology—small, grey, with grey-blue eyes, a big nose and a mouse-face. In her wake, someone carries a map and the skeleton.

She takes her place behind the stove, still rubbing her hands, and begins the lesson. First she questions the students on their homework, then she lectures. Oh, she knows a lot, does Miss Riegel, and she is a clever lecturer, starting with fish and ending with reindeer. Her favorite topic, according to Margot, is propagation, which surely must be so because she is an old maid.

Suddenly she is interrupted; a small wad of paper flies through the air and lands on my desk.

"What have you there?" she asks in an accent that shows she hails from The Hague.[1]

"I don't know, Miss Riegel."

"Come here, and bring that piece of paper with you."

I rise timidly and take the note to the front.

[1] The setting of Anne's tales is, of course, Amsterdam. To the inhabitants of that city, the manner of speech of the people from The Hague sounds affected.—Translator.

"Who is that from?"

"I don't know, Miss Riegel; I haven't read it."

"Ah, so we'll first attend to that."

She unfolds the note and shows me its content—the single word "traitor." I turn red. She looks at me.

"Now do you know who sent it?"

"No, Miss Riegel."

"You are lying."

I feel myself getting flaming red and stare at the teacher with what I know are flashing eyes, but I don't say a word.

"Tell me who wrote that note!" says Miss Riegel, addressing the class. "Whoever did it, raise your hand!"

Way back in the room a hand is raised. Just as I thought—it was Rob.

"Rob, come here!"

Rob now faces the teacher.

"Why did you write that note?"

Silence.

"Do you know, Anne, what it means?"

"Yes, Miss Riegel."

"Explain!"

"Can't I do it some other time? It is a long story."

"No. Explain!"

I tell her about the French test and the zeroes Lies and I got for cheating, and the way we betrayed the class.

"A pretty story! And Rob, did you think it necessary to give Anne your opinion during a lecture? And Anne—I simply don't believe that you didn't know where that note came from. Sit down, both of you!"

I was furious. At home I told the whole miserable story in detail. Some weeks later, I thought I had a justified complaint about the mark Miss Riegel had given me on my report card, and I asked Father to talk to her about it. He came back without an improved mark, but with the information that, by mistake, he had called the teacher Miss Riggle throughout the interview. He further reported that she thought Anne Frank a very sweet girl, and had no recollection of the dear child ever having lied to her!

A Geometry Lesson

HE'S IMPRESSIVE as he stands before the class—a big, strong old man, his bald dome ringed with a wreath of grey. He always wears a grey suit and an old-fashioned high collar, its tips bent outward. He speaks with a peculiar accent; he often mutters and as often smiles. He is quite patient with those who do their best, but loses his temper in dealing with the lazy ones.

Of the ten children questioned, nine give unsatisfactory answers. He takes endless trouble in explaining, clarifying the problems; he reasons with the pupils so that they, themselves, may find the answers. He is fond of posing riddles and, after class, likes to talk of the days when he was president of one of the biggest soccer clubs in the country.

But Mijnheer Heesing and I were often at loggerheads, and always because—yes, because of my talking habit. In three lessons I got six reprimands. This was too much for the master, who, by way of remedy, prescribed an essay of two pages. It was handed in at the next lesson, and Mijnheer Heesing, who could take a joke, laughed as he read it and seemed particularly amused by this paragraph:

"I must, indeed, try hard to control the talking habit, but I'm afraid that little can be done, as my case is hereditary. My mother, too, is fond of chatting, and has handed this weakness down to me. Until now, she hasn't succeeded in getting it under control."

I had been told to write my essay under the title, "A Chatterbox."

But at the next lesson, I again was tempted to whisper a few remarks to my neighbor, and—Mijnheer Heesing took his little notebook and jotted down, "Miss Anne Frank: An essay entitled, 'An Incorrigible Chatterbox.'"

This piece of prose, too, was duly delivered. In Mijnheer Heesing's next lecture, however, I repeated my misdeed, and the master wrote in his little book, "Miss Anne Frank: An essay of two pages, entitled, ' "Quack, quack," said Mrs. Quackenbush.'"

What would you have thought in my place? It was pretty clear to me that Mijnheer Heesing was having a little joke; otherwise, he would surely have given me some stiff geometry problems to do. So I decided to answer his joke with a joke of my own and, with the help of Sanne Houtman, I wrote the "essay" in rhyme. Here is a part of it:

"Quack, quack," said Mrs. Quackenbush,
As she called her big, big brood;
They waddled as fast as ever they could
And gave each other many a push
In their rush to reach their mother's wings.
"Oh, Mama, we hope you have some bread,
For all of us are nearly dead!"
They were very hungry, the poor things.
"Yes, sure," said Mama, "I have your lunch,
Eat this, and I will give you more;
To get it, I had to go ashore,
But, as you see, it was quite a hunch.
I had to steal it, but you be fair,
And each take his honest part."
The little ducklings were pretty smart,
And obeyed the mother then and there.
In doing it, they made a rumpus;
They cried, "Peep-peep" and "Quack-quack-quack."
But who was that with a ruffled back?
An angry swan! Oh, Heaven, help us!

—Etc., etc.

[72]

Heesing read it; read it aloud to the class, also read it to some other student groups, and gave in. From then on, we were good friends; he paid no further attention to my chattering, and never punished me again.

P.S. The long and short of it is that my maths teacher was a very decent sort. The nickname "Mrs. Quackenbush" has stuck to me, and I have Mijnheer Heesing to thank for it.

Paying Guests

WHEN HARD necessity forced us to let our big rear bedroom, we had to swallow our pride; none of us was used to having strangers around the house. The room was cleaned out and refurnished with whatever pieces we happened to have, but these were insufficient for an attractive bed-sitting room. And so Father made the rounds of the auction rooms and slowly picked up a few articles.

In three weeks we had become the owners of a pretty wastepaper basket and a tea table everybody liked, but we badly needed a decent wardrobe and a couple of comfortable armchairs.

Once more Father went out hunting, and this time he took me along. At the auction we sat down on a wooden bench, which was almost entirely occupied by hard-bitten buyers and other unwashed fellows, and waited, waited, waited . . . We could have waited until the next day, for that afternoon they sold nothing but china!

Disappointed, we left. Not very hopeful, we went back the next day for another try. This time we were luckier; Father bid for a good-looking oak wardrobe and a pair of leather-covered armchairs.

To celebrate our acquisitions, we stopped at a tea-room and each had a cup of tea and a piece of pastry. Then, quite gaily, we went home.

But, when the wardrobe and armchairs were delivered, Mother discovered some strange ridges in the wood of the wardrobe. Father, too, took a sharp look and, yes, the thing was full of wood-worm. They don't hand out little leaflets announcing such things at auctions, and the salerooms are generally so dark that you can't see them yourself.

Naturally, the chairs also were given a close examination. It was as we had feared—they, too, had fallen victim to the same sort of vermin.

We telephoned the auction place and urged them to haul away the stuff as soon as possible. This done, Mother heaved a sigh of relief. Father also sighed, but for another reason; he had been told that his poor guilders would not be returned.

A few days later, Father met a friend who had some furniture he didn't use and was willing to lend us until we got something better. So now our problem was solved.

(Here, dumb-bell that I am, I had to stop, since, as everyone knows, I dropped my fountain-pen in the stove. I shall, however, continue with a poor old one.)

Now we stuck our heads together to think up and paint a smart little advertising poster to put in the window of the corner bookshop, for a consideration we had to pay the following week.

Soon people came to look at the room. The first was an elderly gentleman, who wanted a room for his bachelor son. The deal was almost made when the son, who was with him, put in his two cents' worth. What he said was so silly that Mother seriously doubted his sanity. She wasn't far off, for the old man shyly admitted that his son was sometimes given to "wandering."

Mother didn't know how to get those two out of the house quickly enough—but she did. Dozens of people came and went, until one day there arrived a stout, middle-aged chap. As he was willing to pay a good price and seemed to have few needs, he was accepted.

This man was lots of fun and little trouble. Sundays he brought chocolates for us children and cigarettes for the grown-ups, and more than once he took us all to the pictures. He was with us for a year and a half, and then rented an apartment for his old mother, his sister, and himself. Later, when he came to call, he assured us that the time he had lived with us had been one of the nicest periods in his life.

Another advertisement was put in the bookshop window. Again the bell was rung by small and large, young and old applicants. One of them was a fairly young woman in a poke bonnet, and we immediately nicknamed her "Salvation Nell." We let her the room, but she didn't prove as pleasant a guest as the fat man.

First of all, she was very careless and left her room in a mess. Secondly, and this was the worst, she had a fiancé who often got drunk. Once, for example, we were startled by the bell in the middle of the night. Father went to answer, and there stood the fellow, dead drunk. He patted Father on the shoulder and thickly repeated, over and over, "We are good friends, aren't we? Yesh, yesh, we are good friends!" Bang! The door was slammed in his face.

When, in May 1940, Holland was invaded, we asked Salvation Nell to leave and let the room to an acquaintance of ours, a young man of about thirty. This chap wasn't bad, but he had one weakness—he was thoroughly spoiled. Once, in the heart of winter, when we all saved as much electricity as we could, he complained bitterly of the cold. It was badly exaggerated, for the heater in his room was going full blast.

But one has to be indulgent with lodgers, and we gave him permission to use the electric stove once in a while. What was the result? He used it all day long! We begged and pleaded with him to be a little less extravagant, but it did no good. The electric bills went up scandalously, and one fine morning, Mother took her courage in both hands, shut off the electricity, and was not to be found for the rest of the day. Eventually the electric stove was blamed, "It had overloaded the fuse," and the young man had to stand the cold as best he could. Just the same, he, too, lived with us a year and a half, and then he got married.

Again the room was vacant, and Mother was about to dust off our advertising sign, when a friend called and recommended a divorced man who urgently needed a room. He was a tall fellow of around thirty-five, with glasses and an unsympathetic face. Mother didn't want to disappoint her friend, and she took him in. He, too, was engaged, and his fiancée visited us often. The wedding day was not far off when the pair got into a terrific fight, and he suddenly married someone else.

About the same time we moved ourselves, and we hoped to be rid of paying guests for ever!

Dreams of Film Stardom

December 24th, 1943

(This was written as a "secret" answer to the questions of Mrs. Van Daan, who never tired of asking me why I didn't want to become a film star.)

I WAS seventeen, an attractive girl with flirtatious eyes and a wealth of dark curls—a teenager filled with ideals, illusions, and day-dreams. In one way or another, the day would come when my name would be a household word and my picture would occupy a place of honor in the memory book of every damp-eyed film fan.

The questions of how I was to achieve fame and in what field bothered me very little. When I was fourteen I used to think, "That will come in good time," and when I was seventeen I thought so still. My parents were not aware of my grandiose plans, and I was foxy enough to keep them to myself. It seemed to me that I'd be better off, should I ever become a celebrity, to experience things in private before sharing my adventures with Father and Mother. I suspected that they might not be over-enthusiastic about such a turn of events.

Let no one think that I took those day-dreams of mine very seriously, or that I had thoughts for nothing else. On the contrary, I was always industrious in school and, besides, did much reading for pleasure. At fifteen I had finished one of our three-year high schools. Now, mornings, I attended a school that specialized in teaching foreign languages, and in the afternoons, I did my homework or played tennis. One day (it was autumn) I was home cleaning up a cupboard, when, amid a pile of assorted, discarded stuff, I came upon a shoe box, with the words FILM STARS written in large letters on the lid. I remembered that my parents had ordered me to throw this box out, and that I had hidden it carefully so nobody would find it.

Curious, I lifted the lid, took out the many little packages inside, and loosened the elastic bands in which each was wrapped. I got so fascinated looking once more at all the made-up faces, that I was startled when, a couple of hours later, someone tapped me on the shoulder to ask me to come to tea. I was sitting on the floor, surrounded by little stacks of newspaper and magazine clippings.

Later, in straightening my room, I kept the film-star box aside. That evening, I continued my examination—and found something that so impressed me that I couldn't get it out of my mind.

This was an envelope filled with pictures of a family of film actors, in which three daughters were stars. I came across the address of the girls, whose name was Lane. Then and there, I took a piece of paper and a pen and started writing a letter to the youngest of the sisters—Priscilla Lane.

Secretly, I posted the letter, which was in English. In it I told Priscilla that I would love to have a photo of her, and also of both her sisters, and asked her to be good enough to answer me, as I was keenly interested in the family.

I waited more than two months and, though I didn't want to admit it to myself, I had lost hope of ever getting an answer to my letter. There was nothing surprising in this, for I realized that if the Lane girls answered the notes of all their admirers and sent photographs to them, all of their time would have to be devoted to their correspondence. But just then my father one morning handed me a letter addressed to "Miss Anne Franklin."

I hastily opened and read it. My family were very curious and, after I had told them of my letter, I read Priscilla's aloud. She wrote that she would not send photos before she knew something more about me, but that she would be more inclined to do so if I would write her, in more detail, about myself and my family.

Truthfully, I wrote to Priscilla that I was more interested in her personal life than in her film career. I wanted to know, among other things, if she went out much in the evening; if Rosemary had to work as much and as hard as she, etc., etc. Much later she asked me to call her by her nickname of "Pat." Priscilla seemed so pleased with my letters that she answered each one faithfully.

As the correspondence was, naturally, conducted in English, my parents couldn't object, as it obviously provided good practice for me. In her letters, Priscilla told me that she spent most of her days at the studio and gave me an idea of how she divided her time. She corrected my mistakes and sent my letters back to me, on condition that I would return them again to her. Meanwhile she had sent me a big collection of photos.

Priscilla, who was twenty, was neither engaged nor married, which didn't disturb me in the least. I was immensely proud of my friend, the film star.

So passed the winter. In late spring a letter came from the Lanes, in which Priscilla asked me if I would like to fly to the United States and spend two of the summer months as their guest. I jumped for joy, but I hadn't reckoned with the objections of my parents. I couldn't accept the invitation; it was impossible for me to travel alone to America; I didn't have enough clothes; I couldn't stay away that long, and all the other worried notions that occur to loving fathers and mothers on such occasions. But I had made up my mind to go to America, and go I must.

I reported all of the parental objections to Priscilla, and she answered each one to my satisfaction. First of all, I wouldn't have to travel alone. Priscilla's companion, who was visiting relatives of hers in The Hague, would take me with her to the States. As for my return trip to Holland, Priscilla would think of a chaperone when the time came.

My parents still objected: Neither I nor they really knew the Lane family, they said, and it was more than likely that

I would feel entirely out of place in their home. They made me cross; it almost seemed as though they begrudged me this unusual opportunity. I pleaded that it would be almost an insult to decline such a cordial invitation. After they had received a charming and reassuring letter from Mrs. Lane, they finally decided the matter in my favor. I worked hard in the months of May and June, and when Priscilla wrote that her companion would arrive in Amsterdam on July 18th, preparations for my voyage were completed.

On the eighteenth, Father and I went to the station to meet the lady. Priscilla had sent me her photograph, and I recognized her at once among the many passengers. Miss Halwood was a small woman with greying blonde hair, who talked much and rapidly. She looked a sweet person.

Father, who had once been in America and spoke good English, conversed with Miss Halwood, and I ventured a remark now and then. It had been arranged that she would stay with us for a week. That week fairly flew by, and scarcely a day had passed before Miss Halwood and I were friends.

On July 25th, I was so excited that I couldn't swallow a single bite of my breakfast. But Miss Halwood, an experienced traveller, gave no sign of agitation. The entire family saw us off at Schiphol Airport, and finally, finally, my trip to America had begun.

We arrived in the neighborhood of Hollywood on the evening of the fifth day. Priscilla and her sister Rosemary, her senior by one year, met us. As I was somewhat tired from the trip, we drove to a hotel near the airport. After breakfast the next morning, we stepped again into the car, which was driven by Rosemary.

In slightly more than three hours, we reached the Lane house, where I was cordially received.

Mrs. Lane showed me to my room, which was really a charming small apartment with a balcony. This, then, was to be my home for the next two months.

It was not difficult to feel at ease in the hospitable Lane home. Much work and much fun were the daily routine; the three famous young stars, by the way, helped their mother more than I, an ordinary teenager, ever did. I soon got used to speaking English. Priscilla was free during the first two weeks of my stay and showed me much of the beautiful surroundings. Nearly every day we went to the beach, and I gradually became acquainted with people of whom I had heard or read. One of Priscilla's intimate friends was Madge Bellamy, who often went along with us on our sight-seeing jaunts.

Nobody would have judged Priscilla to be older than myself; she treated me as a girl of her own age. When her free fortnight was up, she had to go back to the Warner Brothers studio and—oh, joy!—I was allowed to go with her. I visited her in her dressing-room and saw Priscilla making tests.

She finished early that first day and showed me around the studio. "Anne," she said after a while, "I just got a wonderful idea. Tomorrow morning, you go to the office where pretty girls apply for jobs and ask the man in charge if there is anything you could do. Just in fun, of course."

"Yes, I'd like that," I said. Next day, I really did go to that office. It was a terribly busy place; the girls stood queued up in the hall. I joined the line and in half an hour I was inside the office. But that didn't mean that it was my turn; there were still many girls ahead of me. Again I waited, this time about two hours. A bell rang—this was for me!—and bravely I stepped into the inner office, where a middle-aged man was seated behind a desk. He greeted me in a standoffish manner. Asking my name and address, he seemed surprised that I was a guest of the Lanes. Finished with those questions, he took another good look at me and asked, "I suppose that you want to be a film star?"

"Yes, sir, if I have the talent."

He pushed a button, and in walked a smartly dressed girl, who asked me, with a gesture rather than in words, to follow her. She opened a door, and the sharp light in the room made me blink my eyes. A young man behind an intricate apparatus gave me a friendlier greeting than the one I'd had before and told me to sit on a high stool. He took several pictures, then rang for the girl, and I was led back to the older man. He promised to send me word whether or not I should return to the studio.

Encouraged, I found my way back to the Lane house. A

week later I received a note from Mr. Harwick (Priscilla had told me his name). He wrote that the photos had come out very well, and asked me to come to his office at three o'clock the next afternoon.

Now, armed with an invitation, I was admitted at once. Mr. Harwick asked me if I would pose for a manufacturer of tennis rackets. The job was for just one week, but after I had been told what I would be paid, I gladly consented. Mr. Harwick telephoned the tennis man, whom I met that same afternoon.

Next day I made my appearance at a photo studio, where I was to go every day for a week. I had to change clothes in minutes; I had to stand, sit, and smile continuously; walk up and down, change clothes again, look pretty, and put on fresh make-up. At night I was so exhausted that I had to drag myself to bed. On the third day it hurt me to smile, but I felt that I must keep faith with my manufacturer.

When I came home on the evening of the fourth day, I must have looked so ill that Mrs. Lane forbade me to return to the job. She herself telephoned the man, and got him to excuse me.

I was deeply grateful. Undisturbed, I hugely enjoyed the rest of my unforgettable vacation. As for dreams of film stardom, I was cured. I had had a close look at the way celebrities live.

My First Article

February 22nd, 1944

IMAGINE THAT the subject of my first article knew that he was going to be used as "material"—wouldn't he turn red and ask, "Why me? What's so interesting about me?" Let me put the cards on the table: Peter is my subject, and now I'll tell how that occurred to me.

I wanted to write about somebody, and as I already had described most of the other people in the house, I thought of Peter. The boy always keeps himself in the background and, like Margot, never causes dissension.

If, towards evening, you knock on the door of his room and hear him call a soft "Come in!" you may be sure that, on opening the door, you'll find him looking at you through two of the steps of the ladder to the attic and saying, "So!" in a gentle, inviting tone.

His little room is—what is it really? I think it is a passage to the attic, very narrow, very draughty, but—he has turned it into a room. When he sits at the left of the ladder, there's surely no more than a yard's space between him and the wall. There stand his little table, laden, like ours, with books (a few steps of the ladder also hold some of his possessions) and a chair.

On the other side of the ladder, his bike hangs from the ceiling. Useless at present, it is carefully wrapped in brown paper, but a small chain, dangling from one of the pedals, is still visible. This corner is completed by a lamp with an ultra-modern shade, made from a piece of cardboard covered with strips of paper.

I am still standing in the open door, and now I look in the other direction. Against the wall—that is, opposite Peter and behind the table—stands an old divan, covered with blue flowered stuff; the bed-clothes have been hidden (but not quite successfully) behind it. Above the day-bed hangs a lamp, the mate of the other one, and similarly decorated. A bit farther on, there is a small bookcase filled, from top to bottom, with paper-covered books that could belong only to a boy. A hand mirror is fastened to the wall beside it. Probably because the owner didn't know where else to put it, a small tool chest stands on the floor. (I know from experience that anything in the way of a hammer, a knife, or a screwdriver one may need, can be found in its depths.)

Near the bookcase, a shelf, covered with paper that once was white, was originally meant for such things as milk bottles, but has been converted into an annex of the library; it all but groans under the weight of books. The milk bottles have become neighbors of the tool chest, on the floor.

On the third wall hangs a wooden case that may have contained oranges or cherries, but that now serves as a cabinet for such articles as a shaving brush, a safety razor, a roll of plaster, a small bottle of laxative, etc. Beside the cabinet stands the prize exhibit of the Van Daan family's ingenuity— a cupboard made of cardboard, held together by two or three uprights of some sturdier material. In front of the cupboard there hangs a really handsome curtain, which Peter, after much coaxing, got from his mother. The cupboard itself is filled with suits, overcoats, socks, shoes, and the like. The stuff massed on top of the cupboard is so mixed up that I've never been able to recognize one single item.

The floor coverings of Mr. Van Daan, Jr., also are worth seeing. He has one small and two large genuine Persian rugs of such striking colors that everyone who enters the little room remarks on them. These pieces, which at one time must have cost a great deal, lie on a floor so shaky and irregular that one can't walk on it without the utmost caution.

Two of the walls are covered with green jute, and the other

two are generously plastered with pictures of more or less beautiful film stars and advertising posters. Grease and scorch spots should cause no surprise, for it is to be expected that, with so much stuff in a small space, something or other is bound to get dirty in a year and a half. The beamed ceiling, also, is no longer in good condition and, since there are leaks in the roof and Peter's room is in the attic, he has spread some sheets of cardboard to catch the drips. Innumerable water spots and rings show that this protection is far from adequate.

Now, I believe, I've gone all around the room; I have forgotten only the chairs. One of them is an old wooden armchair of Viennese design with perforated seat; number two is a white kitchen chair which Peter appropriated last year. He started to scrape off the paint, probably with the idea of giving it a fresh color, but he didn't have much luck and stopped. And so, half scraped off, part white, part black, and with only one rung (we used the other for a poker), the chair isn't very pretty. But, as has been said, the place is dark, and the poor wreck doesn't attract much attention.

The door to the kitchen steps is festooned with aprons; there are also a few hooks with dustcloths and a brush. After all this, everyone should know each nook and cranny of Peter's room, but not, of course, the inhabitant himself. And now it's the turn of the owner of all these glorious possessions.

There's a sharp difference in Peter's appearance on weekdays and Sundays. Weekdays he wears overalls, from which he rarely separates himself, as he objects to having the things washed too often. I can't imagine the reason for this attitude, except that he fears his favorite piece of clothing might wear out that way. At any rate, it just has been laundered, and its color—blue—is once more recognizable. Round his neck Peter wears a blue scarf, which apparently is just as dear to him as the overalls. A heavy, brown leather belt and white woollen socks complete his weekday attire. But on Sundays Peter's clothing may be said to undergo a rebirth. Then he wears a handsome suit, a fine pair of shoes, a shirt, a tie—everything that belongs to a young man's nice wardrobe.

So much for Peter's appearance. As for the man himself, I have changed my opinion radically of late. I used to think him dull and slow, but nowadays he is neither the one nor the other. Everybody agrees that he has grown into a fine young fellow. I know in my heart that he is honest and generous. He has always been modest and helpful, and I think that he is much more sensitive than people give him credit for. He has one preference that I shall never forget—the cats. Nothing is too much trouble where Mouschi or Moffi are concerned, and I do believe that those two sense that there isn't much love in his life and try to make up for it.

He's not afraid—on the contrary—and not as smart-alecky as other boys of his age. He isn't stupid, either, and has a remarkably good memory. That he is handsome I needn't say, for everyone who sees him knows that. His hair is wonderful —a wealth of fine brown curls. He has grey-blue eyes, and— describing faces has always been my weak point. After the war I'll paste his photo, together with those of the other people who were in hiding with us, in this book by way of illustration. That will save me the trouble of describing them.

Happiness

March 12th, 1944

BEFORE I begin my story, I'll tell quickly what has happened in my life so far.

I have lost my mother (I've really never known her), and my father hasn't much time for me. When my mother died, I was two years old; my father gave me into the care of a charming couple, with whom I spent five years. So I was seven when I was sent to boarding-school. I stayed there until I was fourteen; then I was, happily, allowed to join my father. Now he and I live in a boarding-house, and I go to the Lyceum. Nothing out of the ordinary happened to me until—until I met Jacques.

We became acquainted because he moved into our boarding-house with his parents. First we saw each other a few times on the stairway; then, by chance, in the park, and after that we went several times for a walk in the woods.

From the first, Jacques impressed me as a splendid boy, perhaps a little shy and withdrawn, though that may have been the very quality that attracted me. Gradually, we had more dates together, and now we often visit one another in each other's rooms.

I had never had a close acquaintance with a boy before, and I was surprised to find him entirely different from the boys in my class, who were boisterous and boastful.

I began to think about Jacques, after thinking a good deal

about myself. I knew that his parents didn't get on together and quarrelled often, and I felt that this must disturb him very much, for a love of peace and quiet was one of his characteristics.

I am alone most of the time and often feel sad and lonely; it's probably because I miss my mother and because I've never had a real friend in whom I could confide. Jacques is in the same situation; he also had only superficial friends, and it seemed to me that he, too, needed someone to take into his confidence. But I couldn't get closer to him and we continued to talk about unimportant things.

But, one day, he came with an obviously made-up excuse, as I was sitting on a cushion on the floor, looking at the sky.

"Do I interrupt?" he asked.

"Certainly not," I said, turning towards him. "Sit down beside me, or don't you believe in dreaming?"

He stood by the window, leaning his forehead against the pane.

"Oh, yes," he said, "I dream a lot like this. Do you know what I call it? Taking a look at the history of the world."

"That's a fine way of putting it; I must remember it."

"Yes," he said, with the peculiar smile that always confused me a little, because I never knew exactly what it meant.

We talked again of trivial things, and after a while he left.

The next time he called on me, I happened to sit in the same spot, and he once more took up his place by the window. That day, the weather was magnificent; the sky was a deep blue (we were up so high that we couldn't see the houses, at least not I, from my spot on the floor); dewdrops clung to the bare branches of the chestnut tree in front of the house, and the sun turned each drop into a sparkling diamond as the branches slowly moved. Seagulls and other birds flew, chattering, past our window.

I don't know why it was, but neither of us could utter a word. Here we were, in the same room, not far from each other, but we scarcely saw one another any more. We looked only at the sky, and talked to ourselves. I say "we," for I am sure that he felt as I did, and that he was making no more effort to break the silence than I.

Fifteen minutes—then he spoke. He said: "When you let beauty and peace sink into you, dissension and strife begin to look like sheer insanity. Everything that people make a fuss about, becomes unimportant. And yet, I don't always feel this way."

He looked shyly at me, perhaps afraid that I might not understand him. I was delighted that he expected me to answer, that I finally had found a sympathetic person to whom I could tell my thoughts.

"Do you know what I always think?" I said. "That it is silly to fight with people about whom you feel indifferent. To differ with people for whom you care, is another story. You are fond of them, and it hurts you more than it angers you when they provoke you."

"Do you really think so, too? But you don't quarrel much do you?"

"No, but enough to know what it is like. The worst of it is that most people go alone through this world."

"What do you mean by that?" Jacques now was looking straight at me, but I decided to persist; perhaps I might be able to help him.

"I mean that most people, married or single, stand inwardly alone. They have no one with whom they can talk about all of their feelings and thoughts; and that is what I miss the most."

All Jacques said was, "It is the same with me."

We took another look at the sky. Then he said, "People who, as you put it, have no one to talk to, miss much, very much. And it is just that realization which so often depresses me."

"No, I don't agree. Nobody can help feeling depressed now and then, but there's no point in anticipating that you're going to be sad.

"You see, what you look for when you are depressed is happiness. No matter how much you miss someone to whom you could express your feelings, happiness, once you have found it and keep it in your heart, can never be lost."

"How did you find it?"

I got up. "Come along," I said, and I went ahead of him, up the stairs, to the attic. There was a storage space with a window. The house was unusually tall, and when we looked out of the window, we saw a great stretch of sky.

"Look," I said. "If you want to find happiness within yourself, you have to go outside on a day with much sun and a lovely blue sky. Or you could stand at a window such as this, and look at our city under the brilliant blue. Sooner or later, you will find it.

"Let me tell you what happened to me. I was in boarding-school, which I never liked. The older I got, the more I disliked it. One free afternoon, I went alone for a walk on the moor. I sat down and dreamed for a while.

"When I looked up again, I realized that it was a glorious day. Until then, I had been so wrapped up in my own gloomy thoughts that I had paid no attention to it.

"From the moment that I saw and felt the beauty all around me, that little nagging inner voice stopped reminding me of my worries. I could no longer feel or think of anything but that this was beauty and this was truth.

"I sat there for about half an hour, and when I got up and walked back to that hateful school, I was no longer depressed. Everything impressed me as good and beautiful, the way it really was.

"Later I understood that, on that afternoon, I had for the first time found happiness within myself. I also realized that no matter what the circumstances, happiness is always there."

"And did it change you?" he asked.

"Yes, it did. I was content. Not always, mind you; I still grumbled from time to time, but I never was downright miserable again. I had learned that most sadness comes from self-pity, but that happiness comes from joy."

When I had finished, he was still looking out of the window and seemed lost in thought. Suddenly he turned and looked at me.

"I haven't found happiness yet," he said, "but I have found something else—someone who understands me."

I knew what he meant. From then on, I was no longer alone.

ESSAYS

Translated by Michel Mok

Give

I WONDER if any of the people sitting in warm, comfortable homes have any idea what it must be like to be a beggar? Have any of those "good, dear people" ever asked themselves about the lives of poor people or children around them? All right, everyone gives a beggar a few coppers now and then. But it is usually pushed hurriedly into his hands, and the door is closed with a bang. And what is more, the generous donor usually shudders at having to touch such a dirty hand. *Is it true, or isn't it?* And then people are surprised that beggars become so rude. Wouldn't anyone, who was treated more like a beast than a human being?

It is bad, very bad indeed, that in a country which claims to have good social laws and a high standard of behavior people should treat each other in this way. Most of the well-to-do people regard a beggar as someone to be despised, dirty and uncared for, rude and uncivilized. But have any of them ever asked themselves how these poor wretches have become like this? Just compare your own children with these poor children. Whatever is the difference really? Your children are clean and tidy, the others dirty and uncared for. Is that all? Yes, that's really the only difference. But if a poor beggar's child were to receive good clothes and learn nice manners, then there wouldn't be any difference at all.

We are all born alike, they were helpless and innocent too. Everyone breathes the same air, a great many people believe in the same God. And yet, yet the difference can be so immeasurably great, because so many people have never realized where the difference really lies. Because if they realized it, they would have discovered that there really wasn't any difference at all. Everyone is born the same, everyone has to die, and nothing remains of their worldly glory. Riches, power and fame last only for a few years! Why do people cling so desperately to these transitory things? Why can't people who have more than they need for themselves give that surplus to their fellow citizens? Why should some people have such a hard time during their few years on this earth? But above all, let the gifts be given kindly and not just flung in their faces; everyone has the right to a friendly word! Why should one be nicer to a rich woman than to a poor one? Has anyone sorted out the difference in character between the two? The true greatness of a person does not lie in riches or power, but in character and goodness. Everyone is human, everyone has his faults and shortcomings, but everyone is born with a great deal that is good in him. And if one were to begin by encouraging the good, instead of smothering it, by giving poor people the feeling that they are human beings too, one would not even need money or possessions to do this.

Everything begins with the little things. For instance, don't only stand up in a tram for the rich mothers, no, remember the poor ones too. Say you are sorry if you step on a poor person's toes as you would for someone rich. People will always follow a good example; be the one to set the good example, then it won't be long before others follow. More and more people will become friendly and generous, until finally poor people will not be looked down upon any more.

Oh, if only we were that far already, that our country and then Europe and finally the whole world would realize that people were really kindly disposed towards one another, that they are all equal and everything else is just transitory!

How lovely to think that no one need wait a moment, we can start now, start slowly changing the world! How lovely that everyone, great and small, can make their contribution towards introducing justice straight away! Just as with so many things, most people seek justice in quite another quarter, they grumble because they receive so little of it themselves. Open your eyes, first make sure that you are always fair yourself! Give of yourself, give as much as you can! And you can always, always give something, even if it is only kindness! If everyone were to do this and not be as mean with a kindly word, then there would be much more justice and love in the world. Give and you shall receive, much more than you would have ever thought possible. Give, give again and again, don't lose courage, keep it up and go on giving! No one has ever become poor from giving! If you do this, then in a few generations no one will need to pity the beggar children any more, because they will not exist!

There is plenty of room for everyone in the world, enough money, riches, and beauty for all to share! God has made enough for everyone! Let us all begin then by sharing it fairly.

Why?

THE LITTLE word "why" has been a very strong thing with me ever since I was a tiny little girl and couldn't even speak properly. It is a well-known fact that little children ask questions about everything because they are unfamiliar with everything. This was very much the case with me, but even when I grew older I couldn't wait to ask all kinds of questions, whether they could be answered or not. This is not so terrible in itself and I must say that my parents tried to answer every one of my questions very patiently, until . . . I began even badgering strangers, and *they* generally can't stand "children's endless questions." I must admit that this can be very tiresome, but I console myself with the idea that there is a saying that "you must ask in order to know," which couldn't be completely true, otherwise I'd be a professor by now.

When I grew older, I realized that it is not possible to ask every kind of question to everyone and that there are many "why's" that cannot be answered. From that time on I tried to help myself by starting to think out these questions on my own. So I came to the important discovery that questions which one mustn't ask can be solved by oneself. Therefore, the little word "why" taught me not only to ask but to think.

Now as to the second part of the word "why." How would it be if everyone who did anything asked himself first, "Why?" I think they would then become more honest and much, much better people. For the best way to become honest and good is to keep examining oneself without stopping. I can imagine that the last thing people like to do is to confess to themselves their faults and their bad side (which everybody has). This is the case with children as well as grown-ups—in that respect I don't see any difference. Most people think parents should try to educate their children and see to it themselves that their characters develop as well as possible. This is certainly untrue. Children ought to educate themselves from their earliest youth and must try to show real character by themselves. Many will think this is crazy, but it isn't. Even a very small child is a little personality and has a conscience and should be brought up by being treated in this way, so that it will feel that its own conscience is punishing it in the harshest way possible. When children reach the age of fourteen or fifteen, every punishment is ridiculous. Such a child knows very well that no one, not even its own parents, can get anywhere with punishments and spankings. By arguing reasonably and by showing the child the mistakes it is making, one would get much better results than by strong punishments.

But here, I don't want to sound pedantic, but only to say that in the life of every child and every man, the little word "why" plays a big part, and rightly so. The saying, "You must ask in order to know," is true in so far as it leads to thinking about things, and by thinking nobody can ever get worse but will only get better.

_I._

Ik heb veel ideeën en ben bezig ze samen te
rijmen tot één geheel. Om een overzicht te
krijgen. en omdat ik anders geen lijntjes-
papier heb, schrijf ik het maar heel achterin

Cady's leven.

1e deel: hoofdstuk I.

Toen Cady haar ogen opende, was het eerste
wat ze zag, dat alles rondom haar wit was.
Het laatste wat ze duidelijk wist was, dat iemand
haar riep..... een auto, toen viel ze ..... en toen
was alles donker. Ze voelde nu ook een stekende
pijn in haar rechterbeen en haar linkerarm en
zonder dat ze het wist kreunde ze zachtjes. Dadelijk
daarop boog zich een vriendelijk gezicht over haar
heen, dat onder een witte kap uitleek.
"Heb je veel pijn kleintje. Herinner je je iets van
wat er met je gebeurd is?" vroeg de zuster.
"Het is niets ....."
De zuster glimlachte. Toen vervolgde Cady, moeilijk
sprekend: "ja... een auto, ik viel .... dan niets meer!"
"Zeg me dan alleen nog even hoe je heet, dan kunnen
je ouders je opzoeken en hoeven ze niet langer in
ongerustheid te zitten!"
Cady schrok zichtbaar: "Maar.... maar, maar eh....-
Meer bracht ze niet uit.

UNFINISHED NOVEL

Cady's Life

Translated by H. H. B. Mosberg

CHAPTER I

WHEN CADY opened her eyes the first thing she saw was that everything around her was white. The last thing she was consciously aware of was that someone called her . . . a car, then she fell . . . and then everything was dark. Now she also felt a stinging pain in her right leg and left arm, and without knowing it she moaned softly. Directly afterward a friendly face looking out from under a white cap bent over her.

"Have you much pain, poor little one? Can you remember anything about what happened to you?" the sister asked.

"It's nothing . . ."

The sister smiled. Cady continued, speaking with difficulty: "Yes . . . a car, I fell . . . then nothing else."

"In that case, just tell me your name now, then your parents can visit you and need no longer be in suspense."

Cady became visibly frightened. "But . . . but, but ah . . ." More she could not say.

"Don't be afraid, your parents have not missed you for long. You have only been with us a little over an hour."

Cady managed a little smile with some difficulty. "My name is Caroline Dorothea van Altenhoven, Cady for short, and I live at the Zuider Amstellaan 261."

"Do you want to see your parents very badly?"

Cady nodded in reply. She was tired and everything was so painful. After a sigh she fell asleep.

Sister Ank, who kept watch near the bed in the small white room, looked anxiously at the pale little face which lay on the pillow so calmly as if nothing had happened. But something had in fact happened. The girl had been run over by a car which was just turning the corner when she wanted to cross the road. The doctor said that she had sustained a double fracture of the leg, a bruise on the left arm, and that something was wrong with her left foot.

Someone knocked softly on the door, and the sister asked a lady of medium height, followed by a particularly tall and good-looking gentleman, to come in. Sister Ank rose. These must be Cady's parents. Mrs. van Altenhoven was very pale and looked at her daughter with frightened eyes. Cady did not notice anything, because she was still fast asleep.

"Sister, do tell us what happened to her. We had been waiting for her for such a long time, and to think she should have had an accident . . . No . . . no . . ."

"Don't worry, madam. Your little daughter has already regained consciousness."

Sister Ank told her now as much about the case as she knew herself; and while she described it as much less serious than it really was, she herself began to feel more at ease and happier. Who knew, perhaps the girl would really get better.

While the grown-ups stood there and talked Cady had woken up, and when she saw her parents in the room she suddenly felt much sicker than when she was alone with the sister. Now thoughts came storming at her. From all sides horrible images came towards her. She saw herself as a cripple for life, one-armed perhaps, and thought of many other terrifying things.

Meanwhile, Mrs. van Altenhoven had noticed that Cady had woken up and approached the bed. "Have you much pain? How are you now? Shall I stay with you? What would you like?"

It was impossible for Cady to reply to all these questions. She only nodded and longed for the moment when all the fuss would be over.

"Father!" was the only word she could manage.

Mr. van Altenhoven sat on the edge of the big iron bed and

without saying a word held his little daughter's uninjured hand.

"Thank you, thank you very much . . ." was all Cady said and then she fell asleep again.

CHAPTER II

A WEEK had now passed since the accident. Cady's mother visited her every morning and afternoon, but she was not allowed to stay long, for she tired the child out with her incessant nervous prattle, and the sister who always looked after her noticed that Cady was longing far more for her father than for her mother.

The sister did not have much trouble with the little patient entrusted to her and although Cady was often in pain, particularly after treatment by the doctor, she never complained and was never dissatisfied.

Best of all she liked to dream away quietly when Sister Ank sat by her bed with a book or some knitting. When Cady had got over the first few days she no longer slept all the time but liked to talk a little. And there was no one she liked to talk to better than Sister Ank. She was calm and always talked softly. It was her softness which attracted Cady. She only now realized that she had always missed this loving and motherly warmth. Thus gradually mutual trust grew up between them.

After the first fortnight was over and Cady had already told her a great deal, Sister Ank asked one morning in carefully phrased words about Cady's mother. Cady had expected this question and found it nice to tell someone about her feelings.

"Why did you ask me that? Did you notice perhaps that I was naughty to Mother?"

"It isn't that, but I sometimes feel that you are different and colder towards your mother than your father."

"You are right. I cannot feel true warmth towards my mother and this has caused me much sorrow. She is so completely different from me. This would not be so terrible in itself, but she shows such little understanding in matters which I find important and which are close to my heart. Couldn't you help me, Sister Ank, and tell me how to improve my attitude towards her so that she does not feel that I cannot love her as much as Father? For I know that Mother loves me, her only child, very much indeed."

"Your mother also means well; I think she simply can't find the right approach. Perhaps she is a bit shy in her own way?"

"Oh no, that's not it. Mother believes that her attitude as a mother is blameless. She would be absolutely amazed if someone were to tell her that she might be using the wrong approach with me. Mother absolutely believes that the fault is mine alone. Sister Ank, you really are the mother I should like to have. I am longing so much for a true mother, and she who is my mother could never take her place. No human being on earth can have things all his own way, although most people think that I lack nothing. I have a cosy home, the relationship between Father and Mother is good, they give me everything I desire, and yet, doesn't a really understanding mother take a very important place in a girl's life? Or perhaps not only in a girl's life? What do I know of the thoughts and feelings of boys? I have never got to know a boy closely. They certainly also need understanding mothers, but perhaps in a different way. No, I suddenly know what Mother lacks. She has no tact. She discusses even the most tender subjects in an ordinary way.

"She does not understand what is happening inside me, and yet she always says she is so interested in youth. She has no idea of patience and softness. She is a woman but not a real mother."

"Don't be too hard on your mother, Cady, perhaps she is different from you, but maybe she has gone through a great deal and prefers to avoid delicate subjects."

"I don't know. What does a daughter such as I know of the life of her parents, her mother's life? Is she told about it? But just because I do not understand Mother and she doesn't understand me there has never been trust between us."

"And Father, Cady?"

"Father knows that Mother and I do not agree. He understands Mother as well as I do. He is wonderful, Sister, and tries to make good what I miss in her. Only he is a little frightened to talk about this and avoids all discussions between us which might touch on Mother. A man can do a lot but he can never replace a mother!"

"I should dearly like to contradict you, Cady, but I can't do it, for I know that you are right. I think it's a great pity that your mother and you are so opposed to one another instead of being allies. Don't you think the situation will improve even when you are older?"

Cady shrugged her shoulders almost unnoticeably. "Sister, I miss a mother so much. I should so much like to have someone in whom I can put my fullest trust and who also trusts me."

Sister Ank looked very serious when Cady had finished talking. "Don't let's discuss this any more now, child. But I think it will do you good that you have told me all this about your mother."

CHAPTER III

THE WEEKS passed by rather monotonously for Cady. She had many visitors, her little friends and acquaintances went to see her, but she was still alone for most of the day. Her health had now improved so much that she was allowed to sit up and read. She had been given a bed-table and her father had bought her a diary. Now she often sat up and wrote down her feelings and thoughts.

She had never imagined that this would give her so much diversion and pleasure.

Life in the hospital was rather monotonous. Every day the same things happened, everything went like clockwork, never a mistake. Also everything was so quiet, and Cady whose arm and leg no longer gave her pain would have preferred a little more bustle and liveliness around her.

Nevertheless, in spite of everything time passed quite quickly. Cady was never bored and everyone gave her games which she could play alone with her right hand. Also she did not neglect certain school books and devoted a certain period of the day to them. She had been here for three months now and soon her stay would be over. Her fractures had not been as serious as first thought, and the doctors thought it better that now that she had somewhat recovered she should go to a sanatorium in the country for a complete cure.

So Mrs. van Altenhoven packed Cady's things the following week, and she and her mother drove for many hours in an ambulance to the sanatorium. Here the days were even lonelier for her. Visitors only came once or twice a week. There was no Sister Ank and everything was strange. The biggest ray of sunshine was her good progress.

When she had quite got used to the sanatorium and the bandage had been taken off her arm she also had to try to walk again. This was terrible! Leaning on two sisters she tried a little, step by step, and the ordeal began anew day by day. But the more she walked the better she succeeded and her legs soon became again used to movement.

It was wonderful when she had recovered so much and could walk so well to be allowed out in the garden in the company of a sister and with a stick. When the weather was good, Cady and Sister Truus, who always accompanied her, sat on a bench in the extensive gardens and talked or read a little when they had taken a book with them.

It had also sometimes happened in the last few days that they had gone for a walk in the wood outside the garden, and because Cady found this much nicer, the sister had no objection to giving her permission. It is true that walking was a very slow process and Cady suffered pain after every unexpected movement, but every day anew she longed for this half-hour in the open when she could imagine a little that she was quite well again.

CHAPTER IV

AFTER THREE weeks when Cady had the path and side-paths at her finger-tips the doctor asked her whether she would like to go out on her own. Cady thought this was wonderful: "Can I really go out on my own tomorrow?"

"Certainly, run away on your own and make sure that we don't see you back here again," the doctor joked.

When Cady was ready to go out she took her stick and went out alone. This was indeed a strange experience. She was so accustomed always to have Sister Truus with her. But on this first day she was not allowed to go farther than the garden fence. After half an hour had passed, the ward sister saw her come in again. Her cheeks were fresher than usual—and she looked happy.

"Well, you liked your walk, didn't you?"

After this day one could see her every day in the garden, and when this was such a success she was also given permission to go a little way outside the fence. The part in which the sanatorium was situated was very secluded. There were hardly any houses in the neighborhood, apart from the big villas which were ten minutes farther away and with ten minutes' walk between them.

Cady had discovered a bench on a side-path, made out of a tree trunk lying on the ground, and she now took blankets with her to make herself comfortable. Every morning she went to sit there to dream and read. Whenever she had taken a book with her, she often laid it down after she had read a few pages, and thought to herself: "Why should I be interested in this book? Isn't it much nicer to sit here and look, isn't it much better to think for myself about the world and its meaning, than to read of the experiences of this girl in the book?" And then she looked around, gazed at the birds and flowers, followed with her eyes an ant which ran away from her feet, carrying a splinter, and was satisfied. Then she dreamt of the time when she could run and jump again wherever she wanted to and discovered that her fall, despite all its misery, nevertheless had its good side. Suddenly Cady realized that here in the wood, in the sanatorium and in the quiet hours in hospital she had discovered something new about herself, she had discovered that she was a human being with her own feelings, thoughts and views, apart from anyone else.

How did it happen that she had never before discovered this, that she had never before thought of thinking about the people who were around her every day; yes, even about her own parents?

What had Sister Ank told her? "Has your mother perhaps gone through so many things that she avoids the delicate matters of life?" And what had she answered herself: "What does a daughter know of the life of her parents?"

How could she have replied so bitterly since she certainly knew that she had never before thought about this question? And yet, would she not now have given the same reply? Was this answer not true? What does a child know of the lives of others, of her girl friends, her family, her teachers, what else did she know of them but the outer side? Had she ever had serious talks with any of them? Deep in her heart, she felt ashamed, although she did not know how to go about finding something out about people. She decided that she would get along better if she trusted them, for then she could help them in their difficulties. And although she realized that she did not know how to help them, she knew at the same time the calm and strength to be had from putting one's trust in someone. She herself had greatly felt the lack of someone to whom she could talk "properly." Was the oppressive loneliness which she sometimes experienced not the same thing? Would this feeling not have been swept away if she had a girl friend whom she could tell everything? And though Cady knew quite definitely that she had fallen short, she knew too that Mother had never sought her out.

Cady was happy by nature and liked to talk, but she did not feel lonely because she had little opportunity of doing it. No, this wasn't it. The feeling of loneliness was of a different nature.

Now she sat there thinking again, "Go on, you are getting dazed, turning this point over and over again in your mind." She gave herself a mental shake, laughing a little, because now that she was no longer given a scolding she probably missed one and was giving it to herself.

Suddenly she looked up, for she heard footsteps approaching. She had never before met anybody here on this lonely path. The footsteps came closer and closer, and now a boy of about seventeen years came out of the wood. He waved her a friendly greeting and immediately walked on again.

Who could he be? She thought, could he live in one of the villas? Yes, he must, for otherwise no one lived here.

Then she dismissed the subject from her mind, and she forgot the boy until he came by again the next morning and for weeks afterwards every morning at exactly the same time.

One morning when Cady was again sitting on her bench the boy came out of the wood, stopped and shook her by the hand, saying: "My name is Hans Donkert. We have really been acquainted for a long time, so why should we not get to know each other?"

"My name is Cady van Altenhoven," Cady replied, and she added, "I think it's very nice of you to stop for once."

"Well, you see, I didn't know whether you would think it crazy of me always to walk past or whether I should talk to you. But lately I have become so curious that I took the risk."

"Do I look as though people would be afraid to talk to me?" Cady asked saucily.

"Well, not now that I see you better," Hans replied to her joke, "but, tell me, I only wanted to ask you whether you have come to live in one of the villas or are you a patient of the sanatorium. That," he added, "seems very unlikely to me."

"Unlikely?" exclaimed Cady. "But of course I have come from the sanatorium. I broke my leg and bruised my arm and foot and now I have six months to recover."

"All that at once?"

"Yes, I was stupid enough to fall under a car, but don't be frightened—you see that even you did not take me for a patient." Indeed Hans had become a little frightened, but he thought it advisable not to pursue this subject further. "I live at Huize Dennegroen, over there." He pointed in the direction. "You will think it strange that I pass here so regularly. I am on holiday and have come home from school, but every morning I go to see my friends, as otherwise I should be bored."

Cady tried to get up, and Hans who noticed this offered her his hand immediately, because she found it difficult. But Cady was obstinate and refused to take his hand. "Don't be annoyed, but I must practice getting up by myself." Hans, who nevertheless wanted to help, then took her book and found this an excuse to take this nice girl back to the sanatorium. Outside the fence they said good-bye as if they had known each other a very long time, and Cady was not surprised when Hans came a little earlier than usual the following morning and sat next to her on the tree trunk. They talked about many things, but these were never of a far-reaching nature, and Cady who found Hans terribly nice was disappointed that she never discussed anything unusual with him. One morning they sat together on the tree trunk a fair distance apart and the conversation was not such a success, something that had never happened before. Eventually neither of the two said another word. They just sat staring in front of them. Cady, though deep in thought, suddenly looked up, feeling that someone was looking at her. For a long time Hans studied the little face next to him, and then their eyes met, and they looked at each other longer than they really wanted to. Then Cady became conscious of this and cast her eyes down.

"Cady," his voice sounded very close, "Cady, can't you tell me what you are thinking about?"

Cady remained silent a little longer, pondering, and then said: "It is so difficult, you won't understand and you'll certainly think me silly." She had become suddenly downcast, and as she finished her sentence her voice died away.

"Have you so little trust in me? Don't you know that I, too, have feelings and thoughts which I don't tell everybody?"

"I didn't mean that I didn't trust you, but it is so difficult. I really don't know myself what to say." They both looked down, their faces were serious. Cady noticed that she had deeply offended Hans and felt very sorry. She suddenly said: "Do you also often feel lonely, even if you have friends in the neighborhood, lonely inside, I mean?"

"I believe that everyone who is young feels lonely now and again. Sometimes it's worse than others. I also feel like that and have so far not been able to talk to anyone about it. Boys confide even less in their friends than girls, and they are even more afraid of being laughed at."

Cady looked at him after he had stopped talking and then said: "I have often wondered why people trust one another so little, why they are so sparing with "real" words? With a few sentences great difficulties and misunderstandings can often be solved."

Again neither of them spoke for a long time, until Cady suddenly appeared to have come to a decision: "Do you believe in God, Hans?"

"Yes, I do firmly believe in God."

"Lately I have thought very much about God but never talked about it. At home as a very small child I learned to pray every evening before going to bed, and I always did this out of habit, just as I brush my teeth every day. I never stayed with God. I mean, that He really never occurred in my thoughts, for whatever I wanted human beings were mostly able to give me. Since I had this accident and have been so much alone I have ample time to think deeply about things. One of the first evenings here I got stuck in my prayers and noticed that my thoughts were completely elsewhere. But then I changed and thought about the deeper meaning of these words and discovered that the apparently simple child's prayer hid far more than I had ever imagined. From that evening I also prayed for other things, things which I myself found beautiful. I did not merely say such a general prayer. But a few weeks later I got stuck in my prayers again one evening and the thought struck me like lightning: Why should God whom I never thought of when I was well help me now when I need Him? And this question worried me, because I knew that in all justice God on His part ought not to think of me."

"I cannot altogether agree with the latter part of what you say. Earlier, when you had a happy life at home, you did not deliberately pray so meaninglessly. You did not think deeply about God. Now that you are looking for Him because you know pain and fear, now that you are really trying to be as you think you ought to be, God will not leave you in the lurch. Trust in Him, Cady. He has helped so many."

Cady looked thoughtfully towards the trees. "How does one know, Hans, that God exists? What and who is God? No one has ever seen Him. Sometimes I have the feeling that all prayers to Him are prayers into thin air."

"If you ask me what and who God is I can only answer this: You can't ask anyone who God is and what He looks like, because nobody knows. Look around you at the flowers, the trees, the animals, and the human beings, then you will know what God is. This wonderful life and death, what is called propagation and nature, that is God. All this He has made the way He has made. You need not have any other image of Him.

"Human beings call this miracle by one name: God. One might just as well give it another name. Do you agree with me, Cady?"

"Yes, I understand and have also thought about it myself. Sometimes when the doctor at the hospital said to me: 'You are making good progress; I am sure that you will be quite well again,' then I was so grateful, and whom apart from the sisters and doctors did I have to be grateful to other than to God? But on other occasions when I was in great pain I thought that what I called God was fate and so went round in circles without ever arriving at an answer. And when I asked myself, what do you believe now? then I certainly knew that I believed in God. Quite often, I ask God's advice and then I know with absolute certainty that I shall receive the only true answer. But Hans, couldn't this reply come from myself, somehow?"

"As I said, Cady, man and everything living has been created by God as it is. The soul and sense of justice also come from Him. The reply which you receive in answer to your questions comes from within yourself and yet also from God, for He has made you as you are."

"Then you mean that God speaks to me, really through myself?"

"Yes, I mean that. Now that we have talked about this, Cady, we have confided a great deal in each other. Give me your hand and let this be our sign, that we will always trust one another, and if one of us has difficulties and would like to tell someone about them, we, at any rate, will both know what to do."

Cady immediately gave him her hand, and they remained sitting hand in hand for a long time. Both of them felt a wonderful tranquillity grow within them.

Since their talk about God, Hans and Cady both felt that they had forged a friendship which went much deeper than any outsider might imagine. Cady had meanwhile become accustomed to writing down in her diary everything that was happening around her, so that she could also describe best her feelings and thoughts, apart from when she was with Hans.

Thus she once wrote: "Although I now have a true friend I am not always happy and merry. Do moods always change so among people? But if I were always happy I could perhaps not ponder sufficiently over all possible matters which are definitely worth thinking about.

"Our talk about God is still fresh in my mind and it often happens that suddenly when reading in bed or, when I am in the wood, I think: How does God speak save through myself? And then an entire exchange of thoughts seems to follow in my little mind.

"I believe that God 'speaks through me,' because before sending people into the world He gives to each one a piece of Himself. This piece constitutes within man the difference between good and evil and is the source of response to their questions. This piece is just as much part of nature as the growth of flowers and the song of the birds.

"But God has also sown passions and desires in human beings, and within all there is strife between these desires and justice.

"Who knows, human beings will perhaps one day listen more to that 'peace of God' which is called conscience than to their desires."

Meanwhile, the times did not improve for the Jews.

In 1942, many of them had their fate decided for them. In July, the boys and girls of sixteen were called up and deported. Luckily, it seemed that Cady's friend Mary had been forgotten. Later, not only the young people but all had to suffer. Cady endured frightful things in the autumn and winter. Evening after evening she heard the trucks drive through the streets, the slamming of doors and the screaming of children. By the light of the lamp Mr. and Mrs. van Altenhoven and Cady looked at one another and in their eyes the question could be read: "Who will be missing tomorrow?"

One evening in December Cady decided to visit Mary and cheer her up a little. That evening the din in the street was worse than ever. Cady rang the Hopkens's bell three times and

Mary came down; when coming down she first looked carefully through the window. She was asked inside where the entire family sat, as it were, waiting, wearing working clothes and carrying rucksacks. All were pale and did not say a word when Cady entered the room. Had they been sitting here like this every evening for months? The sight of all these frightened and pale faces was terrible. Every door slammed outside caused a shock to all who sat here. These door-slammings seemed to be the very symbol of the slamming of the door of life.

At ten o'clock Cady said good-bye. She realized that there was no sense in sitting about like that. She could not help these people who seemed to be in another world and could not cheer them up. The only one who seemed to be bearing up a little was Mary. She winked at Cady from time to time and tried her best to get her little sisters and parents to eat a little.

Mary took her to the door again and bolted it. Cady walked with her torch in her hand towards her apartment. She had not gone more than a few steps when she stood still, listening. Around the corner of the street she heard steps approaching. It sounded like an entire regiment of soldiers. Cady could not see any details in the dark, but she knew only too well who was approaching and what it meant. She leaned against a wall and switched off her torch, hoping that these men should not discover her. Yet suddenly one stopped in front of her, brandishing a pistol in his hand. He stared at her, his arrogant face threatening. "Come along" were the only words he said, and at once she was seized roughly and dragged along.

"I am a Christian girl of honorable parents, sir," she dared to say. She trembled from head to foot and wondered what this ruffian wanted to do to her. She knew she had to try at all costs to make him look at her identity card.

"What do you mean by 'honorable'? Show your identity card." Cady took it out of her bag. "Why didn't you say so at once," the man said, looking at it. "What a gang of scoundrels!" And before she knew what was happening she lay in the street. Furious about his mistake, the German had given the "honorable Christian girl" a good kick. Disregarding the pain and everything else Cady hurried home.

dan Mary? Waren zij niet alletwee hetzelfde?
Wat had Mary dan misslaan? O, dit kon
niet anders dan verschrikkelijk onrecht zijn..
En plotseling zag ze Mary's klein figuurtje
voor zich, in een cel opgesloten, in lompen
gekleed met een vervallen en afgemagerd
gezicht. Haar ogen waren heel groot geworden en ze keek Cady zo droevig en verwij-
tend aan. Cady kon niet meer, ze viel op
haar knieën neer op de grond en huilde,
huilde tot haar lichaam ervan schokte.
Steeds weer zag ze Mary's ogen en haar
blik die smeekten om hulp, hulp die Cady
wist dat ze niet geven kon.
, Mary vergeef me, kom terug......
Cady wist niet meer wat te zeggen of te
denken, bij deze ellende, die ze zo duidelijk
voor ogen zag hoorden geen woorden
meer. En in haar oren klapten de deuren
en hoorde ze de kinderen huilen en
ze zag voor zich een troep ruwe, gewapende
mannen, zoals die ene die haar in de
modder gegooid had en daar tussen
hulpeloos en alleen Mary Mary die hetzelfde was dan zij zelf.

———

After this evening, another week passed before Cady had the opportunity to go and see Mary again. But one afternoon she took time off and did not bother about her work or other engagements. Even before she reached the apartment of the Hopkens family she knew almost certainly that Mary was no longer there and when she eventually stood before the door she found it sealed. Terrible despair then seized her. "Who knows," she thought, "where Mary is now." She immediately turned round and went home. There she ran to her little room and slammed the door. She sank down on the bed with her coat on and thought ceaselessly of Mary.

Why did Mary have to go away when she could stay here? Why did Mary have to suffer this terrible fate when she could know pleasure? What was the difference between the two of them? Were they not both the same? What crime had Mary committed? And suddenly she visualized Mary's little figure before her, locked up in a cell, wearing rags, and with a wizened and emaciated face. Her eyes had become huge and she looked so sad and reproachful. Cady could not stand it any longer. She fell on her knees and wept, wept until her body became convulsed with sobs. Over and over again she saw Mary's eyes and her imploring glance which begged for help, help which Cady knew she could not give.

"Mary, forgive me, come back . . ."

Cady no longer knew what to say or to think in view of all this misery which she saw so clearly before her very eyes, and she could not hear anything except the slamming of the doors and the crying of the children; she saw before her a troop of brutal armed men, such as the one who had thrown her into the mud, and between them, helpless and alone, Mary, Mary who was the same as she herself.

UNFORGETTABLE READING

That's what you'll find in Bantam Pathfinders—sometimes tender, sometimes terrifying, never failing to evoke the wonder and glory of life. You will find it in books like SHANE, Jack Schaefer's haunting portrait of a hunted gunman's friendship with a young boy; in THE BRIDGE OVER THE RIVER KWAI, Pierre Boulle's story of the brilliant officer whose passion for duty led him to perform an almost impossible feat of military genius for the Japanese Army he hated; in THE RED PONY, John Steinbeck's memorable story of a boy's love for a pony; in THE LIGHT IN THE FOREST, Conrad Richter's nostalgic journey into the past of America. You can buy them wherever paperbacks are sold.

ED10—9/66